Hark!

Hark!

The Glad Sound of Cornish Carols

Hilary Coleman and Sally Burley

Francis
Boutle
Publishers

First published by Francis Boutle Publishers
272 Alexandra Park Road
London N22 7BG
Tel/Fax: (020) 8889 7744
Email: info@francisboutle.co.uk
www.francisboutle.co.uk

ISBN 978 1 9999037 0 1

Contents

Foreword

'The Cornish love to sing, especially at Christmas time, and singers emerge from all over to gather at pubs and clubs to sing their special local carols, following a tradition recorded over 200 years ago. There is nothing as uplifting and cheering as voices raised in harmony when another much loved carol strikes up. The idea for this book came about through the authors' love of participating in carol singing and their desire to share this wonderful music with a wider audience, and they are to be congratulated on their achievement'. *Linda Collins*

'A big part of my family's Christmas was the singing of carols – the more harmonies, the more local versions, the more emotion, the better. This wonderful collection joyfully fills a long-established need for a comprehensive and interesting reference work for the Cornish, giving them the opportunity to really baal to 'en at Christmas, confident they have the tunes and the lyrics under their belts … My praise and huge thanks to Hilary and Sally for all their hard work, and to all who played a part in this very worthy venture. Brenda would be thrilled – Give 'er cloth!!' *Sue Ellery-Hill*

'I first met Hilary and Sally in December 2015 when they came to Pencarrow to record the annual Christmas concert of Cornish carols by The Washaway Gallery Choir. I know that since that evening at Pencarrow they have spent many hours travelling, interviewing, and recording other choirs and singers. This book is the result of that hard work and enthusiasm, and I consider it a great honour that I have been invited to play a small part in its production. Happily the tradition of singing the local carols continues in many parts of Cornwall, and if this book gives encouragement for them to be sung again in places where that tradition has lapsed, then Hilary and Sally will have done a great service to Cornish life'. *Peter Meanwell*

Right: Peter Meanwell, Cornish carol collector and conductor of the Washaway West Gallery Choir, 2017

Far right: Carol book collector, Linda Collins, with some of her collection, 2015

Acknowledgements

Thanks to our funders: Cornwall Heritage Trust, The Federation of Old Cornwall Societies, The Red River Singers

And also too: Audrey Aylmer, Barbara Bassett, Bill Thomas, Chris Hill, Chris & Linda Miners, Chris Symons, Clive Maynard, Cornwall Record Office, David Ireland, David Oates, David Thomas, David Wheeler, Denise & Ray Chubb, Ian Marshall, Ian Russell, Ivor Richardson, Janet Townsend, Jill Hocking, Jo Tagney, John Buckingham, John Ellery, Kate Neale, Kathy Wallis, Katrina Geraghty, Ken Downing, Kim Cooper , Kresenn Kernow, Linda Collins, Marion Coleman, Merv Davey, Mike Brown, Mike O'Connor, Mike Richardson, Murray Collins, Neil Davey, Nigel Nethersole, Paul Collins, Patrick Coleman, Paul Scoble, Peter Meanwell, Pip Wright, Rachel Vaughan, Rick Williams, Roger Gool, Roger Nicholls, Rosie Fierek, Roy Thomas, Roy Trelease, Simon Reed, Stella Rule, Stephen Lawry, Stephen Penhaligon, Sue Ellery, Terry Hedge, Terry & Ann Knight, Tracey Worrall, Lyn Barrett, Vic Legg, Will Coleman, William Thomas.

And finally to all the singers around Cornwall!

*Christmas Carols at
Mount Folly,
Bodmin, 1950*

Introduction

'Long ago an inhabitant of Goonbell declared, "We sing carols six months before Christmas and six months after!" The exaggeration of it all goes to express the Cornishman's deep-rooted love for his native carols. Collectively they are for him a heart-felt link with the past.' (K. Pelmear)

Our experiences of Cornish carols

HILARY: *'Having sung many Cornish carols or carols popular in Cornwall over the years (starting with Lyngham as a teenager) I knew how special they were to this part of the world. I loved the canons and flourishes of the eighteenth and nineteenth century composers; the dance feel of the old "curls" – "carol" originally meant to "dance", and bare, plaintive harmonies of the medieval ones.*

As a child I used to go carol singing with my family and a few neighbours around our village, Calstock in the Tamar Valley, these were the standard carols, well-known around Great Britain. However as an adult I wanted to go carol singing in the village I had moved to: Tregajorran, and by then had become aware of many Cornish traditions including the carols. I also needed others to sing harmonies! So the Tregajorran Singers were formed in 1997. We started with "Lyngham", then "St Day" and "Redruth Wassail" and I remember when we first tackled Merritt's Hark the Glad Sound, we were so chuffed to get it up and running! Another carol we learnt was "Awake Ye Nations" which we got from a songbook from our Treggy Chapel, unaware that my Mum and Dad had also picked it up in Australia and were singing it in East Cornwall calling it "Wakey, Wakey"! We now sing twenty five Cornish carols but I am also aware of the many carols sitting unsung in books such as Dunstan's Cornish Song Book, *Inglis Gundry's* Now Carol We, *and Heath's* Old Cornish Carols*'.*

SALLY: *'One of my earliest memories is of standing next to my Dad, Joseph Mills, holding his hand, listening and "feeling" the wonderful harmonies of Cornish carols being sung in his home town of St*

Day. At the time my family lived in Boscastle, and Dad liked to time his Christmas trip "home" to visit family to coincide with the evening that the local boys would be out carolling. He and I would leave his sister's house and walk the short distance to hear these wonderful carols, and I knew that Christmas was on its way.

In the early part of the twentieth century my father's mother would host a gathering each Christmas morning, during which the inevitable Cornish carols would be sung, and after her death the family tradition was kept up by his sister, my Auntie Paula. When we moved back to St Day in the mid 1970s this became part of our Christmas too, drinking and chatting with friends and family, to the soundtrack of *The Season's Best*, by Holman Climax MVC and Mabe Ladies Choir. Before we all left for our own Christmas dinners, there would of course be singing of Cornish carols! Dad had his own copy of the Holman Climax LP, which has 12 carols by Merritt and Nicholas, and it remains part of my Christmas to this day, although I do now have it on CD!

For a time during the 1970s and 1980s, Dad was the Chairman of Carharrack and St Day Silver Band, who would come to his house during their annual carolling around St Day. In later years the Tregajorran Singers would spend an evening at Dad's house singing Cornish carols, and in what turned out to be his final Christmas, the band also came and played carols for him one last time.

My father's carolling memories included singing "Redruth Wassail" while out in a jingle with his grandfather (also Joseph Mills), and when the Tregajorran Singers were learning "Sound, Sound, Your Instruments of Joy" he told me that that had been one of his Father's (Simon Mills) favourite carols'.

Our joint experiences have spanned several worlds of Cornish music – the Traditional Folk/Celtic, the Community Pub Singing, the Choral including Male Voice Choir; the Church and Chapel and even the Brass Band. All these scenes overlap but through them we have come to love all music when it springs from inclusive and community spirited experiences and celebrates our Cornish identity.

We wrote this book because of the uniqueness of these carols, because they are still being sung and because they are still quite local to particular areas. We assumed that everyone knew about this tradition but have increasingly realised they do not (and we include ourselves here!). Over the years there has been a narrowing of the repertoire, with the top three carols, sung in most places, being 'Lyngham', 'Hark the Glad Sound' and 'Lo, the Eastern' and we wanted to show that actually there is a huge diversity. We are delighted to say that this publication is still only a small selection – we have only been able to give a representation of one from each area – there are just so many more!

On our journeying geographically and academically we have found many strong opinions. Some favouring the older carols as being the 'true spirit of the season' before Christianity took too firm a hold. Some are uncomfortable with the carol hymns overlaying our Cornish Celtic roots. Others strongly identifying with these later compositions of the Industrial and Methodist age, seeing them as the true Cornish 'Curls'. Some do not recognise any of these carols as being what they consider the 'proper carols', or through lack of awareness dismiss Cornwall as not having any authentic carolling tradition.

To quote Ian Russell, who is a leading authority on the carols of Sheffield and Derbyshire and set up the non-profit organisation Village Carols: 'Uniqueness does not lie in a repertoire *per se* but in the context of performance of the carols, their provenance, their evolution in local tradition, and the manner of their performance. It is right and proper that local carollers should feel a sense of ownership for their carols'.

It is so important that we, who wish to collect, preserve and celebrate what is happening in a given place and time, try to remain free of prejudices. However, we are all influenced by the culture and era we find ourselves in but we hope that we can offer in this book a positive picture of the rich carolling tradition in Cornwall and also to reclaim our old carols and bring to the fore those that have remained unnoticed outside of the carolling communities. We also hope we can approach our work in a way described by Zadie Smith: 'People can be too precious about their "heritage" about their "tradition" … Preservation and protection have their place but they shouldn't block either freedom or theft. All possible aesthetic expressions are available to all peoples – under the sign of love'. (*Guardian Magazine*)

The plan for the book was similar to our previous publication, *Shout Kernow*, which was to travel to particular places to record the carols being sung *in situ 'where they do belong to be'*, hence 'Hellesveor' in St Ives, and 'Rouse, Rouse' in Padstow, and also on particular occasions or events such as Bodmin Wassail, Picrous Eve and St Just Feast. We also wanted to represent a variety of locations: church, chapel, pub, out on the street, people's houses, etc., to demonstrate that the carols are embedded in the communities. We aimed to select ones that are most popular or meaningful to the area they come

Opposite: Sally Burley, Hilary Coleman with publisher Clive Boutle at the Holyer an Gof award for Shout Kernow, *Waterstones, Truro, 2016*

from or to the people who sing them. Of the strong tradition of carolling in the North of England, Ian Russell writes: 'Most groups are not formal choirs, in the sense that they do not have a conductor, rehearse or sing from music scores, but they do have a loose hierarchical structure. Supported by a leading group of senior carollers, the leader or 'striker' (a term originated from the action of striking a tuning fork) has the responsibility for what to sing, and for pitching it appropriately'. This description could easily fit our experience of carol singing in Cornwall and also ties in with the Cornish phrase of 'strike sound'.

The book contains harmonised scores (as close as possible to what is recorded or written by the composer), two CDs of the songs sung *in situ*, backgrounds to the songs and composers and personal memories of the people who sing them, plus pictures and photos old and new.

Inglis Gundry, writing in his autobiography *Last Boy in the Family*, says: 'The extraordinary thing about Cornish Carols is that each district seems to guard a separate tradition which seems to have nothing to do with that of its neighbours. I am conscious of a number of these traditions but there are probably more of which I have no idea. There is a tradition around Bude … and then there is the Padstow tradition, as in the collection *Strike Sound*, which I had the honour of editing. Quite apart from this there is the tradition of the Redruth-Camborne area which was collected and published in the 19th Century [and] the St. Ives tradition which I came to know when I visited the Halsetown choir. Quite independent from this is the tradition of St. Keverne in the south, which I had the honour of visiting and finding full of independent things. Quite apart from this, Cornish Carols are full of surprises. Who would have suspected that after Davies Gilbert had published his 1825 collection and had expressly said that for the life of him he could not find any more examples of the "old carols" a whole book of Cornish Carols would come to light which must have been sent to him a few years after he had made this statement? But this is what happened'. Gundry is referring to the MSS of John Hutchens, publishing some of these carols in his collection *Now Carol We*.

About Fenten

Fenten aims to answer the need for a reliable and useable source of sheet music, lyrics, live recordings and information about traditional Cornish songs. *Hark!* will add to Fenten's growing resource of material and recordings of performances by community and school groups from across Cornwall. Other publications are: *Lev Krev: twenty four Cornish songs for schools and community groups plus CD* and *Hoolybus: a resource of songs and associated material with learning CD for use in primary schools*, *Dadn an Dor: twelve mining songs and stories from the Red River Singers* and the Holyer An Gof award winning *Shout Kernow, Celebrating Cornwall's Pub Songs*.

Blog – www.shoutkernow.wordpress.com

A Brief History of Carols

Origins and early carols

The original meaning of 'carol' appears to have signified 'a song, joined with a dance, a union frequently found in religious ceremonies … By some it has been derived from *cantare*, to sing and *rola*, an interjection of joy. It was applied to joyous singing and thus to festive songs; and as these became more frequent at Christmas … designated those sung at this feast'. (Sandys, *Christmastide*, 1852)

Carols flourished in late medieval Britain. 'Such songs consisted of an unharmonised melody that alternated verse and burden (refrain) tunes and were most likely related to the carole, a chain dance to verse and burden songs'. (*Encarta Encyclopedia*)

From the 1500s '… the popular carol merged with the folk song and with the broadsides songs sold on streets'. These folk carols include songs such as 'I Saw Three Ships' and a 'Virgin Most Pure'. Under Henry VIII '… being skilled in music and keeping also the Christmas feast with great magnificence, carol singing flourished; and Latin hymns being abolished at the time of Reformation (1517 onwards), the carols became still more in vogue'. (Sandys)

The carol continued to flourish through the 16th century, until its suppression by the Puritans in the 17th century. (The last Wednesday of every month was declared as a fast day during this time and in 1644 Christmas fell on this day!) In 1647 parliament abolished Christmas and other festivals altogether. Even after the Restoration of the Monarchy in 1660 very little was newly written, although both Nahum Tate's 'While Shepherds Watched' and Charles Wesley's 'Hark the Herald Angels Sing' (originally 'Hark How all the Welkin Rings'), were written during this period. Another popular carol written in 1719 was Isaac Watts' 'Joy to the World'. These composed carols began to vary in form during the 17th century, and their texts began to centre on Christmas. This idea was revived by religious reformers in the 1800s wanting to promote devotional hymn singing (see the Carol Hymn section).

However, as is so often the case with the suppression of something it does not disappear but either lies dormant or goes underground and the old carols 'travelled underground and were preserved in folk song, the people's memory of the texts being kept alive by humble broadsheets of indifferent exactitude' (*Oxford Book of Carols*, 1928). This was particularly true in Cornwall: 'it seems that carols survived the puritan interference more effectively in distant Royalist Cornwall than in any other county' (Inglis Gundry, *Now Carol We*, 1966). But the carol was ignored by 'formal' society in the 18th century and was, according to some, on the edge of being lost altogether. In the 18th and early 19th centuries carols were not sung in Church services as they are today, although Cornwall seems to have been an exception. 'Educated and polite society was probably hardly aware of their existence for carol singing was, at that time, much more a folk tradition, which probably only rarely impinged upon the experience of the middle and upper classes' (R. McGrady, *Traces of Ancient Mystery*, 1993).

Until, in 1822, enters our hero Davies Gilbert of St Erth, who published the first collection of *Ancient Christmas Carols,* mainly, it would seem, because he too thought them to be dying out. This was the 'first conscious recording of folk-music to appear in the British Isles'. In his second edition he added some folksongs and dances and 'it is gratifying to think that the first Carols and Folk-songs gathered in Britain came from Cornwall' (Inglis Gundry, *Old Cornwall*, 1962).

Other publications followed including those of William Sandys who observed that the 'practice of carol singing appeared to get more neglected every year'. Both these collections helped to provide material for the well-known *Oxford Book of Carols* published in 1928. These early carols are described by Richard McGrady as 'ballad carols' as they so often have a narrative, paint a picture or have dialogue between people (e.g. 'A Virgin Most Pure'). They also retain the dance-like feel of their origins, often in 6/8 jig time (e.g. 'The Holly & the Ivy'), and many are in either a minor or modal key (e.g. 'Go Your Way Green Leaves').

So, in the middle of the 19th century, just when the carol looked like it would disappear 'scholarly foundations had already been laid and enough music had been published by Davies Gilbert and Sandys to make carol-singing possible among the few educated people who were interested in it'. (*Oxford Book of Carols*)

The problem was that there was limited opportunity for this to disseminate out to the general populace and although broadsheets did continue to preserve the tradition among the common people, W. H. Husk, in his *Songs of the Nativity*, 1868, reported that 'the broadsheet printers find the taste of their customers rather incline towards hymns, mostly those in use amongst dissenting congregations, than to the genuine Christmas carol'. In other words the general population were moving away from the old carols preferring the carol hymns (see next section, Carol Hymns) until the clergy began to take an interest and started to introduce collections of carols to the church. One of whom was Richard Robert Chope who published *Carols for Use in Church* in 1875. The book features an introduction by Baring Gould and both he and Chope encouraged the use of carols in Church: 'The use of this book during the holy seasons of Christmas and Epiphany will bring many a new feeling of delight to those who have never yet heard carols sung in church'. In St Augustine's (Chope's church in London) they sang them up to Lent! He goes on to say: 'in England after the reformation when Latin hymns were abolished carols were commonly sung in churches as now in Cornwall until Epiphany'. Chope had experience of this: 'I, myself joined in singing carols in the

Churches of the West' as recently as 20 years before he worked in London (approximately 1845). Chope came from Bideford, Devon (b.1830) and seems to have knowledge of Cornwall in the mid 1800s. He includes not only several carols from the Davies Gilbert and Sandys collections but also carols he himself knew to be from Cornwall. However, these are more clearly the carol hymns of the 19th century.

Another important collection published in 1871 was *Christmas Carols Old and New* by the Rev. H. R. Bramley of Magdalen College, Oxford, and Dr John Stainer, the organist there. In 1928 the *Oxford Book of Carols* stated: 'The influence of this book was enormous: it placed in the hands of the clergy a really practicable tool, which came into general use and is still in use after nearly 60 years'. This book brought into general use thirteen traditional carols (such as 'I Saw Three Ships') and twenty four more composed by contemporary church musicians (such as 'See Amid the Winter's Snow' by Sir John Goss and 'Good King Wenceslas' by Rev. Dr. Neale). Thus the canon of the 'standard' Christmas carols began.

Interestingly in 1880 Edward White Benson, Bishop of Truro, later Archbishop of Canterbury, created the service now famously known as the Service of Nine Lessons and Carols for use on Christmas Eve. This very first order of service contained eight carols all of which came from Bramley and Stainer's *Christmas Carols Book* (the ninth was 'Oh Come All Ye Faithful' described as a hymn – see below).

The early carols had a new lease of life through the dissemination of these collections by the churches. They even filtered down to the Cornish non-conformist congregation (e.g. for one year, in 1883 at the Flowerpot Chapel in Redruth, they sang 'Good King Wenceslas' in amongst their usual repertoire of local carol hymns!) As society became more secular the tradition was continued through singing in schools too 'The carol is established again … the work that men like Cecil Sharp did for traditional song and dance is being spread to many ends by the primary and secondary schools throughout the country' (*Oxford Book of Carols*). However, what we lost was the knowledge that some of these carols had their roots in Cornwall. These carols also increasingly supplanted the carol hymns that had been so widely popular here.

Carol Hymns

There is a point where carols overlap with hymns. In the eighteenth century, with the growing popularity of hymnody, especially in non-conformist churches, a new form of Christmas music emerged. This is defined by Richard McGrady as the new 'Christian Carol-Hymn' or, because it was so popular in the industrial districts of Cornwall, the 'Industrial Carol' and was influenced by the spirit of Wesley. McGrady describes it as: 'rarely narrative in content, with exception of the major events of the Nativity story, never legendary, nor numerical. Musically its metres are normally more regular [i.e. 4/4 time]. Harmonically the music is normally firmly set in the major, or less frequently minor keys and never has the modal flavour often found in ballad carols'.

In these carol hymns the minor key is almost never found and he adds it would seem that 'the joy of Christmas … could only be properly expressed in the major key'.

This new movement began with the first appearance of 'While Shepherds Watched' in 1700 by Nahum Tate and was later inspired by early pioneers such as Wesley with

'Hark the Herald Angels Sing' and J. F. Wade's 'Oh Come All Ye Faithful' in the 1740s. A whole section in this book is devoted to 'While Shepherds Watched' alone, as here in Cornwall as elsewhere, there are very many versions.

Ian Russell writes: 'Up until 1820 the Church of England decreed that all singing in the church be restricted to metrical versions of the psalms. A few exceptions to this rule were allowed to cover the key episodes from the Gospels in hymns that paraphrased the scriptural text. It is not surprising that the one chosen to recount the Nativity "While Shepherds" with its common-metre form (four lines of alternate eight and six syllables) should have become the most popular text' in the whole of Britain.

Another reason carol hymns became popular was due in part to the rise of Methodism and other nonconformist sects in the early nineteenth century, and here in Cornwall with the immense popularity of Methodism these carol hymns thrived. The boom in mining also saw people travelling from place to place for work and they carried their carols with them (see Diaspora section). Phillip Payton feels this echoes earlier non-conformity in Cornwall:

> 'Christianity in Cornwall has always possessed a peculiarly Cornish stamp, from the days of the Celtic Saints – whose names survive in Church dedications throughout the land – to the modernity of Cornish Methodism. And Cornish Carols are part of this singular tradition, as purely Cornish as the Mediaeval Miracle Plays in the Cornish language, their popularity in the last century [1800s] mirroring the rise of the Methodist movement'.

In 1889 R. H. Heath, an organist from Redruth, published a collection of Cornish carols, some with composers' names, others being 'compositions handed down from father to son'. These carols Heath describes as being 'sung in the highways and hedges' as well as the chapels and churches. The publication of these two volumes seemed to release an outpouring of other publications, such as Leese, Warmington and finally the carols of Thomas Merritt, which can be seen as the apogee of the carol hymns in Cornwall.

> 'In those areas where Methodism was strongest music and singing had their greatest appeal, and notably so at Christmas … local musicians composed tunes themselves and this was the start of a new tradition, with composers such as Thomas Merritt, Thomas Broad, R. H. Heath, W. B. Ninnis and many others providing a wealth of music with the soaring harmonies and "repeats" so beloved of the mining communities' (Old Cornwall Society, *West Briton*, 2015).

These carol hymns were not always seen in a good light. As Ian Russell says: 'From the early nineteenth century this type of sacred music attracted much criticism on the grounds that it was frivolous and decadent. It was systematically denigrated and ousted from official places of worship as a result of the reforming zeal of university-trained clerics from Oxford and Cambridge who saw in its widespread appeal a threat to their authority'. This resulted in the publication of *Hymns Ancient and Modern* in 1861, which sought to standardise hymns throughout the country and contributed to marginalising local hymns and carols. This denigration continued into the twentieth century and a

good example of this is found in the introduction to the *Oxford Book of Carols* in 1928, where it is said that in the latter half of the 1800s 'our churches were flooded with music inspired by the sham Gothic of their renovated interiors. On this music Sir Henry Hadow in his book *Church Music* (1926) said: 'There has probably been no form of any art in the history of the world which has been so overrun by the unqualified amateur as English Church Music from about 1850 to about 1900. Many of our professional musicians at this time stood at a low level of culture and intelligence and were quite content to flow with the stream … Thirty years ago we were perhaps at our lowest ebb. The music was deplorably easy to write, it required little or no skill in performance, it passed, by mere use and wont, into the hearts of the congregation, it became a habit like any other, and it is only during comparatively recent years that any serious attempts have been made to eradicate it'.

Tregajorran Choir and band, 1860, with serpent and ophicleide

The *Oxford Book of Carols* strove to preserve the early carols and folk songs that had been dismissed a hundred years before in favour of carol hymns. On the other hand, carol hymns, however basic or unpolished, made their way into the hearts of the people; they were loved and preserved by them. As Ian Russell says: 'Such was its appeal at grass roots level that the music was given refuge by groups of carollers, who as singers and or instrumentalists kept and nurtured it as part of their Christmas celebrations in homes, pubs and around their villages'.

Certainly in Cornwall they remained immensely popular and it is fair to say that some of the Cornish carol writers of this era showed great skill in composition and the singers in the execution – see, for example, Hellesveor or the Merritt carols.

Instruments

In our research we came across several references to carol singing being accompanied by instruments. The term West Gallery music commonly refers to the psalms, hymns and carols sung and played in churches, as well as nonconformist chapels from 1750 to around 1860. Hymn singing was often seen as a reaction to the previous forms, which were without accompaniment. During this period, many instruments were seen in church and chapel bands: fiddle, clarinet, serpent, flute, cello (also known as viol or bass viol), bassoon, oboe (or hautbois), ophicleide, double bass, cornet, bass horn, fife, trombone, key bugle, sax-horn, euphonium and other instruments that happened to be available. In the early part of the nineteenth century organs became more common, and the old instruments began to disappear in places of worship.

In 1831 in St Ives a barrel organ replaced the old orchestra in one of the chapels, but as it had a repertoire of only ten hymn and psalm tunes, this must have limited the singing quite considerably.! We know that both viols and flutes were in use at St Petroc's church in Little Petherick in 1858, and in 1900 there were still eighteen Cornish parishes using instruments in church.

> 'On one occasion in Feock Church seven bassoons played the bass; and, my inform-
> ant added "when they all closed down on the low F it was like heaven."' (Ralph
> Dunstan, *Tre Pol and Pen*, 1928).

As Thomas Hardy, in his novel *Under the Greenwood Tree*, tells us, church bands were being dismissed and replaced with the now ubiquitous organ; Hardy's church band took their dismissal sadly but with a certain fatalism. In Cornwall, however, although churches were losing their bands, many of the chapels retained them for a few more years, before eventually turning to harmoniums, pianos and organs. Even then, the Cornish musicians were loathe to give up and continued to play for open air carolling.

In the Fore Street Chapel in St Ives music had originally been provided by violins, cellos and 'clarionets', where they took the place of the striker of tunes, until, later on, a pipe organ was installed. In the late 1950s and early 1960s, the St Ives chapel choirs were still using instruments to help with the lining out (singing or playing the first line to give the pitch), although this died away sometime in the mid sixties. Whilst we were at St Ives' Fore Street chapel we chatted to a previous member of their choir who remembered that usually the cornet or clarinet would take the soprano part; the eupho-nium would play the alto part; euphonium or tenor horn the tenor part; and the bass would be played by bassoon or serpent.

A lovely memory comes from a descendant of Tommy Banfield (1910-1990), who was clarinetist and choirmaster at Halsetown Chapel: *'He can't come out 'cos he's blawed straight!'* (Meaning he'd blown too much on the clarinet and had to lie down!)

Diaspora

'Wherever there is a hole in the ground, there's a Cornishman at the bottom of it.' To this well-known saying could be added 'Wherever there is a Cornishman, there will be singing!' The downturn in the mining industry in Cornwall from the mid-nineteenth century onwards led to a huge number of Cornishmen leaving home for foreign shores in search of work; these 'foreign shores' included destinations elsewhere in the UK. Between 1861 and 1901 some 250,000 Cornish left their homes in search of work, going to all corners of the globe: Australia, North and South America, Africa, India, Europe. Often mining, but in other trades and work as well; some never to return, others coming home again, many sending money back to support families left behind. Wherever they went, they naturally took their customs with them, including their love of singing and of carols.

An article by Trevena Jackson, 'The Cornish Christmas', quoted in Payton's *Cornish Carols from Australia*, describes 'the Cousin Jacks preparing for Christmas – the miners practising their carols, the mothers baking saffron cake and the boys and girls decorating the snug, Cornish Cottages'.

Many parts of the world today boast Cornish Associations, and these areas with the descendants of Cornish miners usually have a strong tradition of singing Cornish carols. Grass Valley in California is particularly well known for its choirs who sing the Merritt carols and other Cornish carols every Christmas. Indeed some, South Australia's Little Cornwall (around Moonta and Kadina on the Yorke Peninsula) in particular, have produced their own 'Cornish' carols, composed by the descendants of Cornish immigrants and in the style of our home-grown carol hymns. Payton writes that the carols were still popular in the 20th century on Yorke Peninsula: 'in December 1909 a large crowd gathered at Agery (near Moonta) to "sing the good old Cornish Carols"'.

Although we have found no evidence that these Cornish carols are still sung in Lancashire, the following extract from the preface to Barnicoat's *Old Cornish Carols*, 1927 illustrates the way the Cornish took their carols with them. He describes the finding of some of the manuscripts from his Grandfather's collection:

> 'During a holiday in Lancashire some fourteen years ago [1913] I discovered several in the house of a Cornishman, whose son was organist at one of the local Methodist Chapels, where the carols were practised from MSS, and sung at Christmastide by choirs, mostly descendants of Cornishmen who, 60 or 70 years ago migrated north

Diaspora emigration advert, West Briton, 1839

as pioneers in the iron ore mining industry. They introduced the carols into the Northern Counties'.

A. K. Hamilton Jenkin, in his *Cornish Homes and Customs*, 1934, identifies this place as Dalton-in-Furness, and goes on to say that the carols 'were regularly used each Christmas at the Dalton Methodist Chapel, and no doubt will come in time to be regarded as traditional Lancashire Carols.'

In the 1949 collection by Harry B. Welliver Jr, we see Cornish singers, both men and women, at the Painesdale Methodist Church, Michigan, USA, singing their beloved Cornish carols: 'Hail Sacred Day', and 'Lo He Comes an Infant Stranger' both by Thomas Merritt, along with 'Star of Jacob' by Stephen Nicholas, and others. Welliver tells us in the notes he has made:

> 'Group feeling or membership? – very definitely. Carols have been sung for many years in this area and this particular group has been together for a long time. They were very proud, but humbly so, of their long association in this annual festivity and seemed especially pleased to be making records for permanent preservation. They had NOT seen the carols in print but songs were learnt by rote and are now sung from memory'.

In the introduction of R. H. Heath's book of *Cornish Carols*, published in 1889, he writes: 'Many of the carols were requested by Cornish men and women who had emigrated to foreign parts.' It would seem that the fact that the carols were carried around the world strengthened the tradition at home too.

Kate Neale, who was brought up in Padstow, has been of help with some of our information. She is currently researching the carol traditions of Cornish emigrants for her PhD and has been to South Australia's Copper Triangle of Moonta, Kadina and Wallaroo as well as Adelaide, and visited Grass Valley in California.

> 'I became fascinated with the idea that Cornish people thousands of miles away from their birthplaces were performing the music they had brought with them from home and even more so when I discovered that some of these communities have maintained Cornish musical traditions to the present day'.

Demise & Revival

In the twentieth century two world wars dispersed and killed many of the men who would have known the older carols and also brought a big change to the way of life. The weakening of the primacy of religion throughout the century played a part in the losing of places and occasions to learn and sing carols. By the 1950s there was increased social mobility, and in Cornwall that meant a tide of non-Cornish moving in who would be unaware of the tradition. Thomas Merritt therefore could be seen as the apex of the golden age of carol hymns, although some composers continued the tradition (see Maddern Williams and Donald Broad).

Ian Russell remarks: 'Despite the fact that the vernacular carol tradition has been the dominant form in the countryside for the best part of two centuries or more, it has received scant recognition by scholars – a footnote here, a dismissive paragraph there. Writers on classical/art music rejected it because it broke their musical conventions. They looked instead to the mediaeval carol. Similarly church music historians ignored it because it was associated with the decadence of the unreformed eighteenth-century church. Even folk scholars such as Cecil Sharp objected to it because he thought it too localised, too "composed" and too structured, with its part singing and instrumental accompaniment. Recently this dismissal has been mitigated by some scholars recognition of their significance and the inclusion of a small selection of these carols in the *New Oxford Book of Carols* (1992).'

There are still areas in Cornwall where they flourish, however, as this book asserts. Methodism continued to be strong in Cornwall and compositions continued. A lovely description of these later composers comes from David Oates who sings with Canoryon Trewoon: *'The people who wrote these later carols published them as one off items and then sold them. I suspect when they were written, chapels still had strong choirs and as they were the vehicles for keeping the carols alive would have added any new ones to their repertoire. My great grandfather wrote quite a few and sold them – usually new tunes to old words. His were done on a form of carbon paper and sold for a penny. He must have been reasonably well known as he won a national composition competition and I remember as a child being in a chapel when the choir sang one of his pieces "The Land that Long in Darkness Lay" (*an evocative title!*) and vividly remember old men in the congregation standing to join in and I still have the image of one near me singing with tears streaming down his face, presumably lamenting a life and time long gone'.*

Revivals in Cornwall began almost as soon as the composing diminished – indeed even Heath, writing in 1889, called his collection *Old Cornish Carols*. In 1927 another book called *Old Cornish Carols* was published, arranged by Ben Barnicoat. They were transcriptions from manuscripts belonging to his Grandfather Francis Woolcock (1810-1888) from Tregony. Barnicoat considers these tunes 'copies of earlier MSS in use in the early part of the eighteenth century'. In 1929 Ralph Dunstan published his *Cornish Songbook* and devoted a large section to carols 'of the true Cornish type'. Since then the Old Cornwall Society have done an invaluable service of printing the occasional piece in their magazines and have more recently embarked on a project to reprint or print new collections from each area of Cornwall. From the 1960s onwards with a renewed interest in older texts, Inglis Gundry published *Strike Sound* the well-known book of carols sung at Padstow and both he and Richard McGrady published collections from old manuscripts such as the Hutchens collection and those from Davies Gilbert and Sandys, in 1966 & 1983 respectively. Kenneth Pelmear revitalized some of the carols too, through his collections, as well as an album recorded in Truro Cathedral in 1982. The Male Voice Choirs have also done a sterling job of keeping them alive and have recorded albums along with Ladies Choirs such as the Stithians and Mabe choirs.

The Champion Carol Singers – Wheal Aisy Choir
by Herbert Thomas, *Cornish Songs and Ditties*, 1904

Aw, we are chamshun singers, the great Wheal Aisy choir,
Our Christmas curls es somethin' for to hear;
We've practised till our uzzels es dry an' hot as fire,
An' we're chackin' for some caake and herby beer.
We tuney in the levels, an' sometimes in the gig,
We tuney gone up the ladder-way
An' tes said one night we frightened ould Farmer Benbaw's pig
W'en we sung to drive the piskies all away.
(Aw, you should hear Wheal Aisy choir,
Like diamond tin we shine;
We larn our curls as we set by the fire
In the dry of Wheal Aisy mine.)

W'en the trees es rud weth holly an' the ground es white weth snaw,
We do clear our throats and start upon our rounds –
There's Hacky with es fiddle, a rosinin' es baw,
An' Siah's gaat bass viol maaken sounds;
There's Johnny's flute a tootin' an' Bill's eufonium,
An' Faishaw weth es faather's ould bassoon,
There's trebles, airs, an' seconds, and a boy to bait the drum,
An' our laider with es fork to pitch the tune.

There es Peter Pennyluna with es brassen offelclide
With fifteen keys an' clacken like a stamps,
An' Caleb's tembren sarpent, with a hole thro' es inside –
''Tes enough to make'ee shevver w'en he vamps.
There's Jim Tregay's lil bugle an' Jan Treloar's trambone,
An' Arklaus's bombardon round es waist –
We can play the counters handsome, with bass an' barrytone,
Ontel you'll wonder 'ow the wind do laast.

We can sing " While shepherds" purty, an' "Salute the happy morn,"
An' "I will sing you one O," an' the rest;
Our anchestors did sing thum the saame 'fore we was born,
An' they was sure to knaw w'ich way was best.
We've nawthin' 'gainst the maakers of flam-new curls at all,
But we're too ould to start another rush;
We are champshuns an' we knaw et – tho' we aren't proud chases at all,
We aren't a' used to baiten 'bout the bush.

You can hark outside the Kiddlys, you can paaze about the street,
You can reset every meetin' house, plaise sure,
But a choir like Wheal Aisy you will never, never meet,
Tell you hear our laider knackin' at your door
So git your caake all ready, an' mix the lemonade,
The fiddles must av rosin – so must we;
We will sing 'ee "Hark the herald" an' the curls our faathers maade –
An' the man to pass the c'lection box es me!

Early Carols in Cornwall

Welcome Christmas which brings good cheer
Pies and puddings, roast pork and strong beer.
Chorus: Come let me taste your Christmas beer
That is so very strong
And I do wish that Christmas time
With all its mirth and song
Was twenty times so long

(Hamilton Jenkin, *Cornish Homes and Customs*, 1934)

Hamilton Jenkin, writing in the 1930s, describes a scene of carollers from 'olden times'; 'a week or so before Christmas, the arrival of the "curl" singers was eagerly awaited in the towns and villages, and the surrounding farms. Then on some dark night when the family were seated before the fire blazing cheerfully on the open hearth, shuffling foot-steps would be heard in the outer kitchen, accompanied by the scraping of throats and a voice giving directions in a stage whisper. A minute afterwards a question from the leader; "Are 'ee ready, boys?" would be followed by the order "Sound for it then!" and the voices would be raised in a long drawn out "do-o-o" to try the pitch. This prelimi-nary accomplished, the leader would hastily call forth in a sort of chanting tone the first line of the carol: As I Sat on a Sunny Bank. At the word "bank" the whole choir took up their parts and burst forth in full harmony'. Other carols sung according to Hamilton Jenkin were: 'The First Nowell', 'The Seven Joys of Mary', 'The Holy Well', 'The Holly and the Ivy' and the 'Twelve Days of Christmas'. 'Printed copies of these carols being almost unknown, the singers had either to write out their own parts in MS ... or the parts had to be memorised ... The old carollers always sang in four parts, viz. air (treble), seconds (alto), counter (tenor) and bass'.

An older description of carol singing which seems to corroborate what Hamilton Jenkin describes comes from the *Autobiography of James Silk Buckingham* (1855) – Buckingham was born in Flushing in 1786. 'Christmas carols of the oldest versions extant were familiar to all classes and the church choirs used to make a round of visits to the different towns and villages, to sing them in parts, at the doors of the principal residents before daylight, amid tempest, snow and sleet, while the enjoyment of their own performance seemed to them a sufficient reward … That which carried the balm to female ears and hearts especially, and was by them, at least always most loudly applauded was called the Seven Joys of Mary, a relic probably of the earliest Catholic poetry of this description'.

For more general information on early carols please see the Introduction. However, it is clear that Cornwall has had a long reputation of carol singing that has endured in spite of religious persecution, with events such as the imposition of the English prayer book, provoking the Prayer Book Rebellion, Henry VIII's dissolution of the monasteries or the banning of Christmas celebrations under Cromwell. 'There must have been a strong tradition of monastic music, especially at the great college of Glasney at Penryn but most of that came to an abrupt end with Henry VIII's savage and greedy onslaught on them' (David Oates, *Western Morning News*, 2001).

In his book, *Christmas Carols Ancient & Modern* (1833), Sandys observes: 'In the West of England and especially in the Western parts of Cornwall, carol-singing is still kept up, the singers going about from house to house where ever they can find encouragement, and, in some of the parish churches, meeting on the night of Christmas Eve and singing in the sacred morning'. He adds that 'the natives of Cornwall have been famous for their carols from an early date'. Confirmation comes from William Scawen in his *Dissertation on the Cornish Tongue*, written around 1683, where he records that the Cornish sang carols during the year at 'several times, especially at Christmas, which they solemnly sang, and sometimes used in their churches after prayers, the burthen of them being 'Nowell, Nowell, good news, good news, of the gospel'.

In 1750 Heath describes in his *Account of the Scilly Isles*, that carols were sung in churches on Scilly, 'in the middle of the last century' (i.e. 1600s). This may sound normal to us today but in those days carols were seen as secular and frivolous and therefore not used in more sombre church services. Also, all festive celebrations were banned by Cromwell in the years 1649-1658. It wasn't until the late 1800s that the clergy, such as Chope and Baring-Gould sought to encourage the use of these early carols again (as opposed to carol hymns – see Introduction). Heath remarks that 'formerly, the Christmas feasts were observed with greater magnificence in Cornwall than in any other part of England'.

The carols would have been transmitted orally but broadsides also played a part in their dissemination. In Cornwall, there were two ballad-printers in particular who were known to have printed carols. William Penaluna, born 1780 at Stithians, initially operated in Falmouth around 1810 (along with a John Heard who was responsible for the appearance of the *West Briton*) He ended up as a printer in Helston publishing songs, carols and history books. The Bodleian Allegro archive has a sheet entitled 'Jesus Saviour of Mankind', subtitled 'A Choice Selection of Christmas Carols, Printed and Sold by W. Penaluna'. With a total of fourteen carols, it is elaborately decorated with pictures of Christ and other religious images for the texts of such songs as 'While Shepherds Watched', 'The Moon Shines Bright', 'I Saw Three Ships' and 'Hark the

Davies Gilbert, an early collector of Cornish carols, c. 1823

Herald Angels Sing'. The other Cornish printer who seems to be known in connection with carol-printing is Richard Woolcock who, like Penaluna, worked in Helston and was born in 1822. The carols he printed include 'While Shepherds Watched', 'Angels from the Realms of Glory', 'As I Sat on a Sunny Bank', 'A Virgin Unspotted' and 'Joy to the World'. He also printed some of the Cornish carol hymns too, such as 'Awake Ye Nations'.

Apart from these broadsides little was available in print and two of the first collectors of early carols came from Cornwall: 'The names of Davies Gilbert and William Sandys are justly honoured in all accounts of the history of the carol. They also hold a distinguished place in any record of music in Cornwall. Their books are pioneering contributions to the history of a form of music which, in their own time, was regarded with scant attention. Yet neither was a musician by profession and there is little evidence to show they were accomplished amateur musicians either.' (R. McGrady, *Traces of Ancient Mystery*, 1993)

Davies Gilbert, whose father was a poor curate, was born in St Erth in 1767 as Davies Giddy, but later took the name of his wife (the couple was thereby able to inherit the Sussex estate of her uncle). He became a Member of Parliament for Bodmin, President of the Royal Society and a patron to inventors such as Hornblower, Humphrey Davy and Trevithick. He wrote *Some Ancient Christmas Carols with the Tunes to Which They Were Formerly Sung in the West of England* in 1823 with an introduction. 'The following carols or Christmas songs were chanted … in churches on Christmas Day and in private houses on Christmas Eve throughout the West of England up to the latter part of the late century'. He also describes a typical Christmas occurring at his home, Tredrea, in 1822: 'The day of Christmas Eve was passed in ordinary manner; but at seven or eight o clock in the evening cakes were drawn hot from the oven; cyder or beer exhilarated the spirits in every house; and the singing of carols was continued late into the night. On Christmas Day these carols took the place of Psalms in all the Churches, especially the afternoon services, the whole congregation joining in'.

The other early collector was William Sandys, born in 1792 in London. He initially became a solicitor, but went on to have a varied career, although he enjoyed scholarly and antiquarian research. His family had links with Cornwall which were further strengthened by his marriage to Harriette Hill from Carwythenack at Constantine in 1816. He wrote two books connected with *Christmas: Christmas Carols Ancient & Modern* in 1833, and *Christmastide* in 1852. In both these books appear collections of carols from Cornwall and he says that 'the carols printed in the following pages have been known in Cornwall for nearly 300 years past and have been obtained from old manuscript copies now in my possession, or oral tradition from the singers themselves … and sometimes from aged persons who had been once famed in such capacity … occasionally from private sources, where they had long been preserved in old families'. He adds, 'Several of the tunes appear to have been passed down orally, until some singer fixed them on paper; but even now many of the carol-singers know them only by tradition and descent, which preserve them very faithfully' (These include: 'Remember Oh Thou Man', 'In those Twelve Days', 'The Cherry Tree Carol', 'The Holy Well', 'A Virgin Most Pure', 'God's Dear Son', 'I Saw Three Ships', 'The First Nowell', 'Tomorrow Shall Be My Dancing Day' as well as the words of 'The Waits Carol', 'The Seven Good Joys of Mary' and 'While Shepherds Watched').

Collections of manuscripts handed down in families were common, like those of John Hutchens, which Inglis Gundry reproduced in his book *Now Carol We* in 1966. In 1927 the *Old Cornwall Society Magazine* ran an article by Tom Miners who described another collection: 'Miss Lizzie Holman of Camborne loaned me an old Manuscript book of carols which had been a family possession for some generations. The book, which runs to about 50 leaves of parchment, contains the words of 23 carols, with an index, and it is carefully written throughout in an old fashioned script, with flourishes and ornamental flowers at the beginning and end of each carol. On the title page the original owner's name is given: "Margery Hocking, Her Book of Carrols, Dec 9th 1797"'.

Towards the end of the nineteenth century interest in old folk songs began and the Folk Song Society was founded in 1898. Collectors such as Baring-Gould and Cecil Sharp also recorded carols. Cecil Sharp visited Cornwall in 1913 and collected versions of the 'Holly and the Ivy', 'Holy Well', etc. This interest continued and in the 1930s Hamilton Jenkin wrote: 'Unfortunately these carols are almost entirely neglected by the modern chapel choirs, and were it not for the work of the Old Cornwall Societies their very existence would be in danger of being forgotten'.

We see that these early carols were favoured at that time over the then more modern, carol hymn. In *Christmas Carols Ancient & Modern* (1833), Sandys also includes the carol 'Hark, Hark What News' as an 'example of how carol singers harmonised their songs. The inclusion of this carol gives us a link between the early carols and the new carol hymns such as those printed by Heath at the end of the century. For example, it has some simple fugues which were popular at that time but not found in these early carols.

CHRISTMAS CAROLS,

ANCIENT AND MODERN;

INCLUDING

THE MOST POPULAR IN THE WEST OF ENGLAND,

AND THE AIRS TO WHICH THEY ARE SUNG.

ALSO SPECIMENS OF

French Provincial Carols.

WITH AN INTRODUCTION AND NOTES.

BY

WILLIAM SANDYS, F.S.A.

LONDON:
RICHARD BECKLEY, 42, PICCADILLY.
1833.

Title page of Christmas Carols, Ancient and Modern, *William Sandys, 1833*

Can Dilly (The Dilly Song)

'Chres'muss edn't like a used to be, fifty er sexty 'ear agone. Well we ait an' ait an' we drinked an' we drinked, till poor ol 'Sol wus glazin' wuss than ever. Some of th' party wus bravish singers, so when somebody called fer a curl, they singed Lo the Eastern fine; ace, proper! Then Mester Trevenen started up Come and I Will Sing You and tooked the solo part.'
(W. Arthur Pascoe, 1929, *Old Cornwall Society Magazine*)

The name of this Twelfth Night carol comes from the Cornish language, with *can* meaning song. However, the term *dilly* is a little more troublesome. In 1790 William Pryce, of Redruth wrote in *Archeologica Cornu-Britannica* that the word *dilly* meant remission or slacking (similar in meaning to the colloquial *dilly dally*). In 1910 H. E. Piggott collected a version of this song from James Alexander Osborne at Treliske, near Truro, and in a letter to Baring-Gould, stated that *dilly* was a Cornish word for riddle. The word *dilly* is known across the UK (as in 'Lavender's Blue, Dilly, Dilly'), and has perhaps migrated from English to Cornish or vice versa, or may even be derived from an older Brythonic word. Ralph Dunstan tells us in his *Cornish Song Book*: 'The mythical Dilly bird was supposed to come only at Christmas and was "never seen but heard-O".'

> 'As far back as I can remember, I with all the other members of our family had a special bun, made in the shape of a bird, to eat on Christmas Eve. My Mother and her brothers and their parents, uncles and aunts had always done the same. My Great-grandparents, when the saffron cake was being made, used to pick out pieces of the dough, make them into this bird shape and bake them. Then each member of the family was given one and the Dilly Carol was sung. My sister gave such buns to her children and my niece, who lives with me, says "yes, I remember that lovely bird"'.
> (J. Kelynak, *Old Cornwall Society magazine*, 1959)

In the song words there is also reference to the gillyflower which may relate to a Cornish variety of apple; Sally's parents-in-law grew various Cornish apple varieties including Gillyflower at Crofthandy.

This carol is part of a large and very old family of songs and is related to the well-known 'Twelve Days of Christmas' and 'Green Grow the Rushes O!' In its many varied forms it is known across the UK, and abroad; there are countless versions from Cornwall alone. Sally's father remembered singing a version of it as a youngster in St Day in the 1920s, and the song is mentioned in C. C. James' *History of Gwennap*, in two forms, having being sung in the Gwennap/St Day area.

Known all over Cornwall as a Methodist hymn, it is also known in America, carried there by Cornish immigrants. In 1889 a Rev J. H. Hopkins heard children singing it, who had 'caught it by ear from Cornish miners employed in the copper mines' on the southern shore of Lake Superior. A. L. Rowse, in *The Cornish in America*, also tells us that it was being sung by the miners on Lake Superior adding that it had been sung in Cornwall for generations as a part-song, often between a woman and a man. Cecil

*Tracey Worrall &
Frances Bennett
with the
traditional
Twelfth Night
cakes at Degol
Stul, 2017*

Sharp heard it sung in the Appalachian Mountains; in 1946, it was recorded in Wisconsin being sung by John Persons, an American-born Cornishman aged 87; it is also in the Max Hunter Folksong collection recorded in Arkansas and Missouri between 1959 and 1969. In the UK it has been recorded in various forms by many collectors including Lucy Broadwood and Baring-Gould. In Cornwall, George Gardiner collected it from C. L. Hart-Smith, in February 1905. Inglis Gundry includes a more religious version in his *Canow Kernow*, as well as a version in Cornish. Forms of this song are known in many languages including Flemish, Breton, Moravian, French-Canadian and Hebrew.

Sandys, in his *Christmastide*, 1852, says of this song: 'There is a Breton song, said to be as old as the fifth century, arranged as a dialogue … which is similar in idea and construction to the carol beginning In Those Twelve Days. It is called Ar Rannou (or Le Series in French) and is in the "dialecte de Cornouaille". Both are counting down songs although the subjects vary.'

The version used in this book was sung at the Degol Stul (Twelfth Night) celebrations at Heartlands, Pool, on January 7th 2017, by the Red River Singers and others, and is the version from Baring-Gould's *Songs of the West*, published in 1905. Baring-Gould talks about numerous versions and styles of this song and says that he chose the least religious, most pagan one to publish. Most of the surviving versions have religious words, but even then it is still often known as the 'Dilly Carol' or 'Can Dilly'.

Although many forms of this song have twelve verses, ours has just ten, and unusu-

The Twelfth Night King and Queen, Matt Blewett and Ruby Livingston, Degol Stul, 2017

ally our version has rhyming couplets where most of the others have single lines, it therefore bears most resemblance to a version Baring-Gould collected from James Parsons from Lewdown in 1888, and also one collected from a serving girl at Horrabridge.

It is Ralph Dunstan that links the song to Twelfth Night, saying it was 'generally sung by three singers at or about the time of Twelfth Night – in West Cornwall'.

Twelfth Night or Epiphany is the twelfth night after Christmas, and is an important date in many folk traditions, and is often associated with wassailing. It is usually celebrated on 6th January in the modern calendar, although the date does vary, according to tradition, in different areas, depending on how the calendar change has been interpreted. In Cornish, Degol Stul means Twelfth Night, though it is not a literal translation. The first Degol Stul *nos lowen* dance night was held in Porthtowan Village Hall in January 2002, and was organised by Cumpas, a Cornish music charity run by Hilary Coleman and Frances Bennett, to celebrate a full twelve months of *nos lowen* dancing at the hall. *Nos lowen* means 'happy night' in Cornish (similar to the Breton *fest noz* meaning 'night festival'), and is Cornish dancing simple enough to join in with, without instruction. Over the ensuing years, the Degol Stul festival has been held in Porthtowan, Grampound, and Pool. This year's festivities, 2017, saw the reintroduction of an old Cornish custom, that of baking a cake containing two dried beans. Those who find a dried bean in their slice of cake are crowned King and Queen for the night!

Can Dilly (The Dilly Song) TRADITIONAL arr. H.Coleman

CD 1 Track 2

Chorus

Come and I will sing you, what will you sing me? I will sing you one - o,

what will you sing me?

what will you sing me?

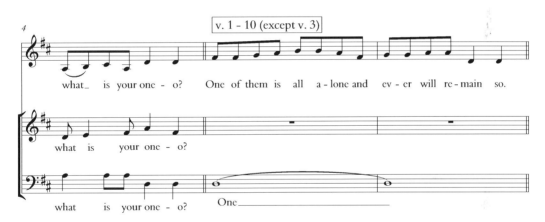

4

v. 1 - 10 (except v. 3)

what is your one - o? One of them is all a - lone and ev - er will re - main so.

what is your one - o?

what is your one - o? One

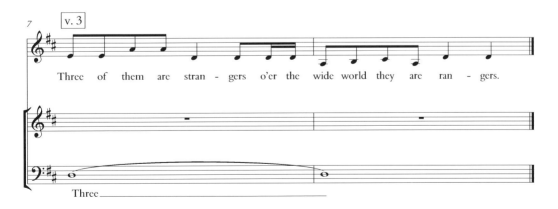

7

v. 3

Three of them are stran - gers o'er the wide world they are ran - gers.

Three

EARLY CAROLS IN CORNWALL

Can Dilly (The Dilly Song)
As sung by singers at Degol Stul, Heartlands, Pool, January 2017

1. Come, and I will sing you.
What will you sing me?
I will sing you one O.
What is your one O?
One of them is all alone, and ever will remain so.

2. Come, and I will sing you.
What will you sing me?
I will sing you two O.
What is your two O?
Two of them are lily-white babes, and dressed all in green, O.
One of them is all alone, and ever will remain so.

3. Come, and I will sing you.
What will you sing me?
I will sing you three O.
What is your three O?
Three of them are strangers, o'er the wide world they are rangers, etc.

4. Four it is the Dilly hour, when blooms the gilly flower, O.

5. Five it is the Dilly bird, that's never seen, but heard, O.

6. Six the Ferryman in the Boat, that doth on the river float, O.

7. Seven it is the crown of Heaven, the shining stars be seven, O.

8. Eight it is the morning break, when all the world's awake, O.

9. Nine it is the pale moonshine, the pale moonlight is nine, O.

10. Ten forbids all kind of sin, from ten again begin, O.

Go Your Way Green Leaves

This carol comes from a collection of manuscripts written down by John Hutchens, which was intended to be included in Davies Gilbert's book. However, these manuscripts reached him too late and were never printed until over a hundred years later when Inglis Gundry included some of them in *Canow Kernow* in 1966. He also produced a later publication, *Now Carol We* (1976), which presented twelve carols from the Hutchens manuscripts. Gundry says 'The 84 pages contain words for 39 carols. Only 27 of these have tunes (melodies alone) but the remainder are marked "to the tune of" some other carol in the collection. Unfortunately, I was persuaded, rather against my will to add 4-part harmony, which slows down the melodies and prevents them from speaking for themselves. I do not think it added to the sale of the book, which is now out of print'.

In his biography, *The Last Boy of the Family*, Gundry describes how he found out about the manuscripts:

Portrait by Bob Hunt of Inglis Gundry, writer, composer and publisher of Cornish carols

'My friend Eric Tappe, hearing me mention Davies Gilbert, had said: "I know a Miss Davies Gilbert". It turned out that she was the great-grand daughter of the very man who had done so much to revive Cornish Carols in the early nineteenth century. She showed me the very book that had been sent to her great-grandfather. Moreover, she allowed me to take it away and make a copy before returning it to her. It was a book written out by John Hutchens from the St. Erth district and it had probably been sent to Davies Gilbert about 1827, too late for him to use. Nothing is known about John Hutchens, except that he copied the carols from an old book so that they were considered ancient in the early nineteenth century'.

The surname Hutchens is common in the St Buryan area.

The meaning of the words is uncertain. The original text of the first line is '... those branch's tree'. However, Gundry says this 'hardly makes sense, so it has been amended. It's possible, however, that this carol was in existence as a popular song before it was adapted to Christianity'. The 'branch's tree' could possibly be the original words and his supposition that this was a popular song originally is borne out by the fact that in 1580, William Byrd wrote an instrumental exploration of a popular tune called 'Greening of the Leaves'. The words of the song were 'the leaves be green, the nuts be brown they hang so high they will not come down' .This seems to have evolved into a children's rhyme, found in America:

'The leaves are green, the nuts are brown, they hang so high they won't come down. Leave them alone till frosty weather, then they will all come down together'.

Boilerhouse singers with Rick Williams, third from the left

It could well be connected with the old song 'Here We Go Gathering Nuts in May'.

Our arrangement of the carol is by Rick Williams from Newlyn. He discovered it in *Canow Kernow* and liked the tune so arranged it for his six men *a capella* group Boilerhouse, so named after the corridor of an inn at Pendeen where the miners sang as they shared out the wages. He likes the more folk approach to music, saying of Boilerhouse: *'we haven't got a conductor ... there's the notes on the page and how you get to them is your own business! So this [carol] fitted into that ... it had that old-fashioned repetitive thing where you don't even have to think about what the words are as long as you can count up to three then you're laughing! With Boilerhouse I want to give them some new stuff and reinforce stuff that is in danger of dying out.'*

Rick, Boilerhouse and others sing carols in the Penzance area and we recorded them singing at the Dock Inn in 2015. It was hot and crowded with an expectant atmosphere and the people there seemed really enthusiastic to join in with the core singers. *'Opinions vary as to how the Dock session started. Sometimes you can't remember how things started, they just happen. Les Rowe brought some people down from the Engine at Nancledra, We [Newlyn Male Voice Choir] used to go down the Dolphin for whatever reason, I don't know why it came to an end. These things have a shelf-life. So then we used to go in the Queens Hotel, with Newlyn Choir on Christmas Eve, that was always a bit genteel! Then we ended up in the Dock, I suppose that was the early nineties, perhaps late eighties. So there was no break it just moved on. I know there's been no break from when I started in something like 1978. The Boilerhouse sprang from that, we thought "this is stupid, we only sing once a year, and, we've got all this desire to do it", so then we started meeting in this kitchen here [Newlyn], January of 2004,5,6 something like that. In the Dock, ten, twelve years ago it was in danger of sounding like a football crowd, so somebody had to go "hang on a minute" and start reintroducing some old harmonies, "and while we're about it these carols are good too, let's do these as well". We used to get "sing something we* know", but the past few years because we've been able to establish the strong harmonies again, it's an entity that stands up by itself so we don't get that anymore! There's a critical mass of people now who are able to give the impression this is something that's a goer. That's why I put all this effort into reviving some and reinforcing the harmonies'. (Rick Williams)

Some of the older carols Rick was able to introduce came from old recordings of the Halsetown Choir in the 1950s and the Pendeen Miners Choir in 1942. (see Pendeen version of 'While Shepherds Watched')

Go Your Way Green Leaves TRADITIONAL

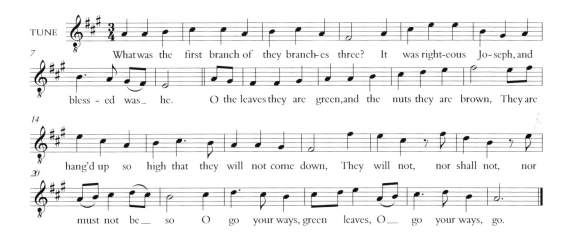

Go Your Way Green Leaves
As sung at the Dock inn, Penzance December 2015

1. What was the first branch of they branches three?
It was righteous Joseph and blessed was he.

Chorus:
O the leaves they are green, and the nuts they are brown
They are hang'd up so high that they will not come down
They will not, nor shall not, nor must not be so
O go your ways, green leaves, O go your ways go.

2. What was the second branch of they branches three?
It was Virgin Mary and blessed was she.

3. What was the third branch of they branches three?
It was our Lord Saviour and blessed was he.

Go Your Way Green Leaves TRADITIONAL arr. R. Williams
(with the tune divided between the tenor parts)
CD 1 Track 3

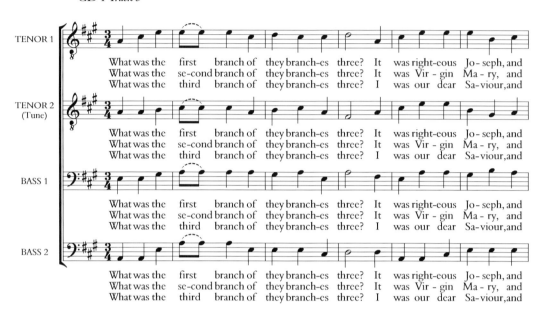

TENOR 1

What was the first branch of they branch-es three? It was right-cous Jo- seph, and
What was the se-cond branch of they branch-es three? It was Vir - gin Ma- ry, and
What was the third branch of they branch-es three? I was our dear Sa-viour, and

TENOR 2 (Tune)

What was the first branch of they branch-es three? It was right-cous Jo- seph, and
What was the se-cond branch of they branch-es three? It was Vir - gin Ma- ry, and
What was the third branch of they branch-es three? I was our dear Sa-viour, and

BASS 1

What was the first branch of they branch-es three? It was right-cous Jo- seph, and
What was the se-cond branch of they branch-es three? It was Vir - gin Ma- ry, and
What was the third branch of they branch-es three? I was our dear Sa-viour, and

BASS 2

What was the first branch of they branch-es three? It was right-cous Jo- seph, and
What was the se-cond branch of they branch-es three? It was Vir - gin Ma- ry, and
What was the third branch of they branch-es three? I was our dear Sa-viour, and

Chorus

bless - ed was_ he.
bless - ed was_ she. O the leaves they are green, and the nuts they are brown, They are
bless - ed was_ he.

bless - ed was_ he.
bless - ed was_ she. O the leaves they are green, and the nuts they are brown, They are
bless - ed was_ he.

bless - ed was_ he.
bless - ed was_ she. O the leaves they are green, and the nuts they are brown, They are
bless - ed was_ he.

bless - ed was_ he.
bless - ed was_ she. O the leaves they are green, and the nuts they are brown, They are
bless - ed was_ he.

hang'd up so high that they will not come down, They will not, nor shall not, nor

hang'd up so high that they will not come down, They will not, nor shall not, nor

hang'd up so high that they will not come down, They will not, nor shall not, nor

hang'd up so high that they will not come down, They will not, nor shall not, nor

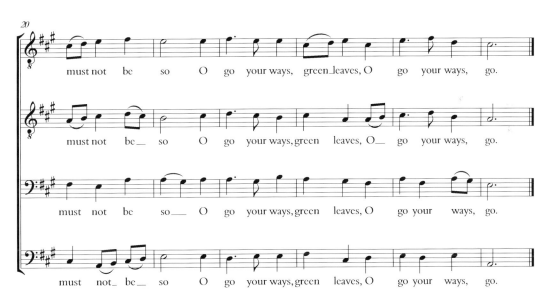

must not be so O go your ways, green leaves, O go your ways, go.

must not be so O go your ways, green leaves, O go your ways, go.

must not be so O go your ways, green leaves, O go your ways, go.

must not be so O go your ways, green leaves, O go your ways, go.

The Holly and the Ivy

We recorded Kescana singing this carol at their rehearsal in a warm kitchen, in Lostwithiel, on a dark rainy night. They began in 1989 called the Tywithiel Singers, a mixture of people from Tywardreath and Lostwithiel. They adopted the name Kescana later, which means 'singing together' in Cornish. Jo Tagney, their musical director adds:

'We began just because we wanted to sing together really, and several of us were mothers with young children, and it was very hard to arrange baby-sitting to go out to choirs, So we all came together and brought our babies with us and sang. We didn't think about performing at all, just a chance to sing together with our friends. We started with pub songs, like "Lamorna", "Little Eyes", "Cadgwith Anthem". We didn't start singing Christmas Carols until we did Nadelik [A Cornish Carol CD with Merv Davey & Pyba in 2002]. *So when we did that we had a nice little group of Cornish mediaeval carols, which started us off really; "The Holly and the Ivy" and "The Cherry Tree Carol"; and "Three Ships", and "Redruth Wassail" we sang in Cornish'.*

Although they didn't intentionally set out to be a women-only singing group, their sound is quite unique, and rather beautiful. It's really striking to hear just unaccompanied women's voices. Kescana have always preferred the more Celtic or mediaeval songs which lend themselves to their approach of making up their own harmonies.

The words come from an old broadside sheet probably around 1710, but are presumably older as there are so many mediaeval 'Holly and Ivy' songs and carols known. It is clearly related to the 'St Day Carol'. Husk's *Songs of the Nativity* (1864) includes the 'Holly and the Ivy': *'This carol appears to have nearly escaped the notice of collectors, as it has been reprinted by one alone, who states his copy to have been taken from "an old broadside, printed a century and a half since," i.e. about 1710. It is still retained on the broadsides printed at Birmingham'.* We presume Husk is referring to Sylvester's 1861 collection *A Garland of Christmas Carols*.

However, these early nineteenth-century sources did not provide music for the carol but Bramley and Stainer's collection *Christmas Carols New and Old* of 1878, coupled the words to an 'old French carol'. It wasn't until 1911 that Cecil Sharp's collection *English Folk-Carols* established the current words and the most well-known melody for the carol. Sharp writes that he heard the tune sung by Mrs Mary Clayton at Chipping Camden.

Our tune's origins, however, are more uncertain. It is very similar to one collected in 1952 from Peter Jones in Herefordshire by Maud Karpeles, which was made popular by the Spinners and Steeleye Span in 1972. Ours is a variation of this (almost a harmony) and does appear in Kenneth Pelmear's *Cornish Carol* book (1982) as 'a Cornish traditional melody'. However Dunstan's collection in 1927 uses the old French melody from Bramley and Stainer. It is not clear if this was sung in Cornwall at that time or was one of the carols he added as possibly being of 'Celtic origin which are worthy of general acceptance'.

As well as Kescana we recorded the Cadgwith Singers singing our version, who said 'we've always sung it like that'. One of the Kescana singers, Jan, said of this version: *'I learnt the "Holly and the Ivy" at junior school, at Alverton in Penzance. That would have been between 1963 and '69, something like that. Fifty years ago! We knew them both, we'd sung the other one as well; but we also sang that one. So, it was a Cornish song! Back then, down in Penzance it was like a different world to what it is now! We sang "Lyngham" and the "St Day Carol" but we didn't know it was anything out-of-the-way. Didn't know it was Cornish. We weren't taught our history at all!'*

A completely different melody was collected by Sharp in Camborne with variations from three different singers, one in 1913 and the others in 1924 and 1926. His informants, Tom Miners and J. E. Thomas, collected yet another melody and words in 1924, from a Mr S. Landry in Callington, which combine the 'Holly and Ivy' words with the 'Cherry Tree Carol'.

As to the meaning of the carol, holly and ivy were powerful male and female symbols in pagan times and they retain some of this magic during the Christmas season when the old Winter Solstice custom of decorating the house with evergreens continues. However ivy is only mentioned in the first line of the first verse and not at all in the 'St Day Carol'. In both carols, the Holly is associated with the Virgin Mary. Although holly was usually seen as a symbol of maleness in this context it is possible that its other association with goodness is intended. There is a suggestion that the words as we know them were changed or Christianised from a more pagan origin and also that the chorus may have been added around the same time. These changes could also account for the loss of any reference to the ivy in the subsequent verses.

There are many references to the making of a traditional Kissing Bush in Cornwall

Opposite:
Cornish Kissing Bush from Old Cornwall *journal, 1966*

Below: Kescana Singers from Lostwithiel

and this one comes from *Old Cornwall*, the journal of the Federation of Old Cornwall Societies: 'The Cornish Bush was made by interlinking two wooden hoops at right angles and tying them firmly together; the hollow globe of four curves thus formed was covered in twists of red crinkled paper and decorated along the staves with holly, ivy or other evergreens. I have heard it called the "Kissing Bough". Fruit such as red apples and oranges were added, and the sparkling shining balls unknown in earlier days. Our presents also adorned the dainty structure, which was hung in a window. One red candle inside at the base was lit after dark and I recall this once caused a near-tragedy by setting the whole thing ablaze so no candle after that!' (C. F. J., *Old Cornwall*, 1966).

The Holly and the Ivy TRADITIONAL arr. Kescana

CD 1 Track 4

The Holly and the Ivy

As sung by Kescana , Lostwithiel, November 2016

1. The holly and the ivy when they are both full grown
Of all the trees that are in the wood the holly bears the crown

Chorus:
Oh the rising of the sun and the running of the deer
The playing of the merry organ, sweet singing in the choir

2. The holly bears a blossom as white as lily flower
And Mary bore sweet Jesus Christ to be our sweet saviour

3. The holly bears a berry as red as any blood
And Mary bore sweet Jesus Christ to do poor sinners good

4. The holly bears a prickle as sharp as any thorn
And Mary bore sweet Jesus Christ on Christmas day in the morn

5. The holly bears a bark as bitter as any gall
And Mary bore sweet Jesus Christ for to redeem us all

6. (repeat first verse)

St Day Carol

'St Day became a place of pilgrimage second only to St Michael's Mount, as proved by the number of bequests to the chapel. It lay on the main route to the Mount. Norden (writing in 1584) says of it "St Daye, a hamlet: there was sometime a chapel, now decayede, called Trinitye, to which men and women came in times paste from far in pilgrimage. The resorte was so greate, as it made the people of the Countrye to bring all kinds of provision to that place; and so longe it continued with increase, that it grew and contynueth a kinde of market to this daye, without further charter"'. (*Old Cornwall*, 1949, Rev J. H. Adams). John Norden (c. 1547-1625) was an English cartographer and antiquary.

One of Sally's earliest memories is singing the 'St Day Carol' at Boscastle CP School, where they called it the 'Sans Day Carol', and her father politely but firmly told her that it should be called the 'St Day Carol', and why. The memory has never left her, and she has made it a personal mission to ensure that as many people as possible understand why it bears that name.

The carol was first collected by W. D. Watson in the early 1900s in St Day from the singing of Thomas Beard, who was then aged between 50 and 60. Richard Blewett who was head of St Day school from 1921-1943, learnt the carol from Mr Beard and passed it on to the children in the school, where generations of children continue to learn it. One of these children was Sally's father.

Watson, a fluent Cornish speaker learnt the language from his mother in Mylor, translated the carol into Cornish adding the verse starting 'As blood it is red' as 'It seems likely to have existed.' (Watson, *Old Cornwall*, 1926). This verse was added as the third verse, and is still sung in that position in some places. Locally it is sung as the last of the four verses, perhaps because it was added to what was already well-known. There are two variations in English of this verse; 'as red as the blood … who died on the rood' (as in Dunstan) or 'blood it is red, then trust we our Saviour who rose from the dead' (as in Kenneth Pelmear). It is the second that is most commonly sung throughout Cornwall, and, presumably, as Kenneth Pelmear lived in Carharrack and later St Day, this was the version he heard people singing.

Watson published it, in Cornish, in April 1926 in *Old Cornwall* under the title 'Carol Kelinen Sans Day. Traylyes dho'n Kernuack gans W. D. Watson.' (Translation: St Day Holly Carol. Translated into Cornish by W. D. Watson.) This was the first time that the carol was seen in print. It was subsequently given to Ralph Dunstan, in English, by Rev Canon Gilbert Hunter Doble and published in Dunstan's *The Cornish Songbook*. Hunter Doble (1880-1945), was born in Penzance and was curate of the parish of Redruth from 1919 until 1925. He was both a Cornish historian and a hagiographer, and, in June 1924, was responsible for the first performance (in English) of the Cornish miracle play *Beunans Meriasek* since the Reformation. He was also instrumental in the revival of the Hal-an-Tow event at the annual Helston Flora Day. Doble also passed the carol on to the editors of the *Oxford Book of Carols* in 1928, where it was titled 'Sans Day

Carol' and although the footnotes explain that it came from St Day in Cornwall there was no mention of this title being in the Cornish language and this has led to the naming controversy. As the Grand Bard Merv Davey says: *'It clearly should either be "St Day Carol" in English or "Carol Sen Day" in Cornish or "Carol Kelinen Sans Day" if you wanted to respect Watson's "pre-unified" Cornish.'* The name 'Sans Day Carol' has resulted in a disconnection of the song from the village of St Day and indeed from Cornwall itself. The carol is very popular in the United States where it is also known as the 'Sans Day Carol'; this might be because the American folklore and song collector James Madison Carpenter (1888-1983) visited Britain between 1929-35 and recorded Watson singing it. Only a handful of items from his collection were ever published. Whatever its name, this carol must surely be one of the first to be translated into and sung in Cornish during the resurgence of interest in the language in the early part of the twentieth century. It seems to have remained in the Cornish language song repertoire, in various forms, ever since. The Skinners Bottom Glee Singers were recorded singing it in Cornish by Peter Kennedy in 1956, and it is not infrequently heard sung in part or entirely in Cornish today, not only by language enthusiasts but also by church choirs, Male Voice Choirs and others.

Opposite: Carharrack and St Day Silver Band, 2017

Above: Boys collecting holly in the Bodmin area, December 1939

It has been suggested that it had been originally sung in Cornish, but changed into English at some point as knowledge of the Cornish language dwindled. Certainly the tune, with its 3/4 time-signature and dancey feel seems to be one of our older carols. The words, a mix of the obviously Christian with the more pagan references to holly, seem to suggest an older origin, possibly with the words modified to incorporate a more acceptable religious element.

Carharrack and St Day Silver Band, under the current leadership of local man, Roy Trelease, seem to have become unofficial guardians of their carol, and unlike most of the rest of the Brass Band community continue to call it St Day (although it seems to be published under the ubiquitous 'Sans Day' title in Brass Band books). The band go car-olling around St Day every year on the Friday before Christmas, and end the evening in the town square, between the Christmas tree and the town clock, where people sing carols along with the band and the parish council and WI provide hot mince pies with clotted cream. Roy always introduces the carol as 'our carol'. He told us: *'The band has gone carolling around the two villages* [St Day and Carharrack] *since it was formed* [in the early twentieth century] *and used to play on Christmas morning. This stopped in the 1950s, and from then on the band just went around the streets as we do today. About fifteen years ago I helped to organise the carolling in the square after going around St Day, and singers first joined us about ten years ago making a really good evening! It is part of Christmas!'*

It is worth noting that the holly is the traditional Christmas tree in Cornwall, and is still used, in preference to the fir tree, by some people today. There is a reference to this in an article in *Old Cornwall*: 'In every cottage would be seen a holly Christmas tree, hanging in the front window as ours still does. Except among the big houses the German fir-tree was not seen in Cornwall and the old traditional holly bough was uni-versal, decorated with home-made tinsel apples and, if it could be afforded, an orange in the centre. In some churches there are holes bored in the tops of the old oak pew end. Notably at Talland, but I do not think it unique, the holes are of two characters … every third pew had a large hole to hold candlesticks, holly and ivy would be wound up the sticks. The second are gimlet bore-holes into which sprigs of holly and ivy would be alternately stuck.' (C. F. J., *Old Cornwall*, 1966)

St Day Carol TRADITIONAL arr. Ian Marshall

CD 1 Track 5

St Day Carol
As sung in St Day Square, December 2015

1. Now the holly bears a berry, as white as the milk
And Mary bore Jesus and wrapped Him in silk

Chorus:
And Mary bore Jesus Christ, our Saviour for to be!
And the first tree in the greenwood,
It was the holly, holly, holly!
And the first tree in the greenwood,
It was the holly.

2. Now the holly bears a berry, as green as the grass
And Mary bore Jesus, who died on the cross

3. Now the holly bears a berry, as black as the coal
And Mary bore Jesus, who died for us all

4. Now the holly bears a berry as blood it is red
Then trust we our Saviour, Who rose from the dead

Carol Kelinen Sans Day
as translated by W D Watson, 1926

1. Ma gron war'n Gelinen, 'ga lyu yu lethwyn,
 Ha Jesu 've mayles en dillas ourlyn

Burdhen:
Ha Mam o an Maghteth, Marya, Mam Dew,
Ha gwedhen a'n gwella
an Gelinen yu. Kelin, Kelin!
Ha gwedhen a'n gwella
an Gelinen yu.

2. Ma gron war'n Gelinen, 'ga lyu yu gwelswer,
Ha Jesu 've crowses: E Vam en awher

3. Ma gron war'n Gelinen, 'ga lyu y gosruth,
Ma Jesu 'gan Selwyas ; enno yu gan fyth

4. Ma gron war'n Gelinen, 'ga lyu y glowdhu,
Ha Jesu 've marow; dredho ny a vew

A Virgin Most Pure

This carol appears in many collections and is very well known around Britain and America. Both the Davies Gilbert and Sandys publications contain 'A Virgin Most Pure', with lyrics that slightly diverge from each other. Gilbert has seven verses, while Sandys gives eight. But both Gilbert's and Sandys' texts differ from other versions and Sandys' words are closest to the earliest known version printed, which, in 1661, was called 'In

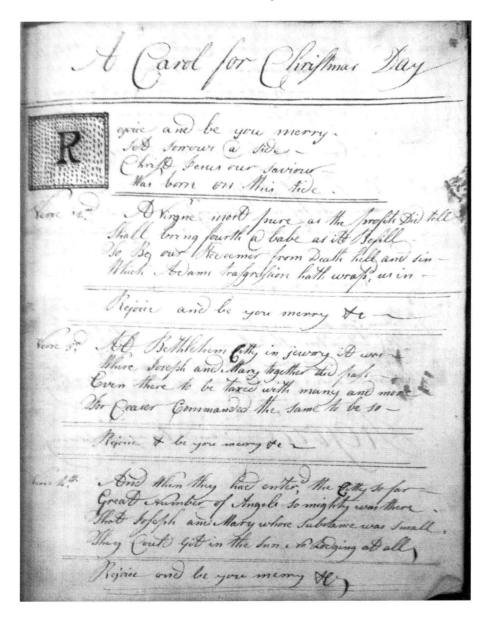

Words to 'A Virgin Most Pure' in a late 17th century notebook, probably from the Hayle area

Bethlehem City' and printed in *New Carolls for this Merry Time of Christmas* in London. The Sandys version from 1833 is much closer to this original than was that of William Knapp, who published a version in 1743 in London, and it is Sandys' version of the words that are sung in our recording.

An old notebook in the Cornish Studies Library which dates from the late 1700s, has the carol words written down. It is from the Rowe collection, and most likely came from the Hayle area; Gilbert came from St Erth. This perhaps shows the popularity of the carol in that area.

As for the melody, Davies Gilbert and Sandys also give a similar tune to each other but both of which are unrelated to that of Knapp, and indeed to many other versions of the carol printed elsewhere. Their version, however, has been reprinted in many of the important carol collections such as Bramley and Stainer, Husk's *Songs of the Nativity*, *University Carol Book* by Eric Routley and in the *Oxford Book of Carols*. Eric Routley observes, in his book *The English Carol* that 'Gilbert's … is the more unusual and attractive, but Sandys' is a rollicking good tune.' It would seem that Gilbert's is the earliest known version of our tune, reproduced and adapted many times.

The carol 'A Virgin Unspotted' was a development of this carol and the earliest version is published in *The Compleat Psalmodist* 1741 by John Arnold. Hutchens has a version of 'A Virgin Unspotted' in his manuscripts, so it was known in Cornwall too.

Hilary began the Red River Singers in 2012, with the aim of introducing the Cornish pub songs, folk songs and carols to a wider group of people. *'We rehearse in Pool and because we're in the heart of the mining area we have developed quite a repertoire of mining songs which we recorded underground in 2014. We are at present learning a whole raft of fishing and sea songs connected with Cornwall for our next publication. However, the Cornish carols have always featured prominently in our repertoire and from October to January we work on our growing collection. We like to sing the ancient carols such as the Virgin Most Pure as well as the more well-known carol hymns'.*

Their arrangement is by Richard McGrady, who moved to Cornwall in 1973 to become music lecturer in the Department of Extra Mural Studies of the University of Exeter. In 1993 he wrote *Traces of Ancient Mystery, The Ballad carols of Davies Gilbert and William Sandys* for the Institute of Cornish Studies. He also wrote *Music and Musicians in Early Nineteenth-Century Cornwall – The World of Joseph Emidy – Slave, Violinist and Composer.*

On the first Sunday of every month the Red River Singers sing, with others, at the Countryman pub in Piece. It is a free house and Nick Lake, the landlord has ensured that the pub has kept its character, with a welcoming atmosphere and a good selection of beers and ciders.

A Virgin Most Pure TRADITIONAL arr. R. McGrady

CD 1 Track 6

1. A—— vir—gin most pure as the pro——phets do tell Hath
2. In Beth'—lem in—— Jew—ry a Ci——ty there was, Where
3. But—— when they had en—ter'd the Ci——ty so fair, A——
4. Then were they con—strain'd in a sta——ble to lie, Where

brought forth a—— ba—by as it hath be—fell, To
Jo—seph and—— Ma—ry to—geth—er did pass, And
num—ber—— of—— peo—ple so migh—ty was there; That
hor—ses—— and ass—es they us'd for to—— tie; Their

be our Re—deem—er from Death, Hell—— and Sin, Which
there to be tax—ed with ma—ny—— and more, For
Jo—seph and—— Ma—ry whose sub—stance was small, Could
lodg—ing so—— sim—ple they took it—— no scorn, But——

Chorus

A—dam's trans—gres—sions Have wrap—ped us—— in.
Cae—sar—— com—mand—ed the same should be—— so. Aye, and
find—— in—— the Inn there no lodg—ing at—— all.
'gainst the—— next morn—ing our Sa—viour was born.

there - fore be you mer – ry,   Re - joice and be you   mer – ry, Set   sor - rows a –

side,   Christ   Je – sus   our__   Sa - viour   was   born   on   this__ tide.

A Virgin Most Pure

As sung at the Countryman Inn, Piece 2016

1. A virgin most pure as the Prophets do tell
Hath brought forth a baby as it hath befell
To be our Redeemer from Death, Hell and Sin
Which Adam's transgressions have wrapped us in.

Chorus:
Aye and therefore be you merry
Rejoice and be you merry
Set sorrows aside
Christ Jesus our Saviour was born on this tide

2. In Bethlehem in Jewry a city there was
Where Joseph and Mary together did pass
And there to be taxed with many and more
For Caesar commanded the same should be so.

3. But when they had entered the city so fair
A number of people so mighty was there
That Joseph and Mary whose substance was small
Could find in the inn there no lodging at all.

4. Then were they constrain'd in a stable to lie
Where horses and asses they used for to tie
Their lodging so simple they took it no scorn
But against the next morning our Saviour was born.

5. The King of all kings to this world being brought
Small store of fine linen to wrap him was sought
And when she had swaddled her young son so sweet
Within an ox manger she laid Him to sleep.

6. Then God sent an Angel from Heaven so high
To certain poor shepherds in fields where they lie
And bade them no longer in sorrow to stay
Because that our Saviour was born on this day.

7. Then presently after the shepherds did spy
A number of Angels that stood in the sky
They joyfully talked and sweetly did sing
To God be all glory our Heavenly King.

Carol Hymns and Hedge Choirs in Cornwall

The Carol Choir
The Down-long Round – Christmas Eve
(John T Barber, *Cousin Jack Afloat – Ashore*, 1969)

We joined the Fore Street carol choir
The night was crisp and clear
Then started off at Virgin Street
With Cully's 'Hellesveor'.

'Andsome it was and no mistake
The great bass deep and rich
The altos and the tenors too
Were good and true to pitch.

One dear old chap there standing by
Said, "Well I must confess
It's like an organ, iss it ez,
An organ, nothing less."

We worked The Digey, through Love Lane
It still continued dry
Did Bunker's Hill and Bailey's Lane
Then on to Chy-an-Chy.

Past Doble's Wall, on up Dick's Hill
Still singing clear and sweet
Turned right at top of Island Square
Next stop Teetotal Street.

Our voices now were rather hoarse
The clarinet gone flat
So all agreed to do Carn Crows
And leave it go at that.

This section is by far the largest in the book because on our travels the majority of carols sung were in this style or came from this period – spanning from 1700s through to the twentieth century! Another reason this section is important is that outside of Cornwall and its diaspora many of these carols are undocumented and the composers unknown; anyone singing Cornish carols would find it hard to believe that this could be the case for our beloved Thomas Merritt!

The definition of carol hymns is dealt with in the history of carols at the beginning of the book but some information about the carols and their composers within Cornwall needs to be written, if only to bear testament to the proliferation and popularity of them here.

Methodism

John Wesley first visited Cornwall in 1743 and visited a further thirty-two times before his death in 1791.

> 'The explosion of religious fervour which took place during the early years of the nineteenth century in Cornwall seems to have been unique, not just because of the implications for behaviour in society but because it appears to have been mixed with a kind of struggle for self-determination – where organisation was concerned, at the least – within the religious community; and this was not a feature of revival across the country. Indeed, as far back as Wesley, it is recorded that he admonished the Cornish people as being far too independent and not willing enough to subscribe to and be governed by the dictates of Wesleyism *per se* – his ideas and his kind of control'. (R. Brown, www.mustrad.org.uk, 2003)

This is one of the reasons why, when the carol hymn was beginning to diminish in other parts of Britain, in Cornwall its style continued to flourish and prompted Philip Payton to assert that:

> 'The great era of the carol in Cornwall was from 1850 until 1900. Old words and tunes were set down on manuscript, often for the first time while new composers arose to write new carols – or to set existing Methodist hymns to new tunes. A distinctly Cornish form emerged; Pelmear noted that "A florid air, frequent word repetitions and a large flowing bass were the chief characteristics of this form of carol".' (P. Payton, *Cornish Carols from Australia*, 1984)

It is hard to imagine in our secular age just how important and integral to life the Church or chapel were, not only from a religious perspective but a social one too. The singing of carols at Christmas was indeed part of this experience as Pelmear states: 'within the chapels themselves, overflowing carol services – no matter how large the

Front cover of Barnicoat's collection of carols from Tregony Manuscripts, 1927

building – were the order of the day. Christmas day that is – and at six o'clock in the morning!' Within Redruth town itself there were at least four large Methodist chapels: the Wesleyan, the Bible Christian, the Primitive and the United Methodist Free Church which was the largest, built in 1865, and had a seating capacity of 1,600.

Redruth

In his book *Victorian Redruth,* the historian Michael Tangye writes:

> 'From the mid to late Victorian period Redruth became recognised as the centre of music in Cornwall. It is quite obvious that the inspiration for its description in 1887 as the "musical metropolis" stemmed from the influence of Methodism. Local chapels, filled to capacity, were led by large choirs trained by talented musicians to perform to a high standard. A Redruth correspondent described this great love of music and singing in 1875: "Song is the heritage of our mining population. Song gushes from almost every miner's open door, it flows from every eminence, it is heard everywhere, the live long day and late at night, and there are those who even sing in their sleep. Cornish miners have filled the world with song. Nowhere could you hear so excellent music or singing"'.

Miners were key to Redruth becoming the centre of this explosion of music and for its dissemination around Cornwall and beyond:

> 'It is interesting to see that many composers lived in Redruth and Illogan. One must remember that the Redruth area was very densely populated owing to the miners working there and a large number of chapels were built to accommodate them. It was in these chapels that the new compositions were sung with much fervour'. (*West Briton*, Martin Matthews, 2004)

Ralph Dunstan was born in 1857 and died in 1933 in Carnon Downs and he believed that 'The Redruth-Camborne carol is the true Cornish Curl … the carols of this type were mostly composed in the great mining district stretching from Gwennap and St Day to Redruth, Illogan, Camborne, Chacewater, Baldhu and Twelveheads, and they spread in all directions to Helston, Truro, Perran and the clay districts round St Austell'. Although his book, *Cornish Carols*, was published in the 1920s his knowledge of carols came from a time long before that, as he was in his early seventies when it was published. He differs from Payton by asserting that the 'golden age of production was from 1790 to 1850'. And adds, 'it is this type of carol which was carried during that period by Cornish miners to every part of the world, and which is probably more sung at this present time [1920s] in the Cornish homes far away than in most parts of Cornwall itself.'

Kenneth Pelmear goes further to suggest that these carols had their roots in the western mining parish of Illogan and that Thomas Broad was the granddaddy of them all: 'Thomas Broad and J. Coad both from Illogan, were responsible for developing the style and they were followed by many others – most of whom were simple miners, fishermen or agricultural labourers … From Padstow to Newlyn, Stratton to St Just, traditions established themselves. Groups, for instance, both large and small – often singing, sometimes playing – took their music to village square and town market-place.'

This belief that they spread from there across Cornwall is only partly true as there were composers in other areas creating carols in similar styles. However, it is true to say that Redruth had an outpouring of music which no doubt inspired others, demonstrated by the following account from the *West Briton* in 1889. One gets the feeling that the composers, who were most often the organists from each chapel, were trying to outdo each other, and must have seemed like the pop stars of their day.

> 'Notes from Redruth: Carol singing this season promises to be well to the fore. Bands of young men sometimes known by the not too euphonious soubriquet of 'hedge choirs' have been promenading the streets singing the time-honoured carols in a more or less melodious manner. This has been going on for several weeks past, principally on Sunday evenings. At the Wesley Chapel the carols to be sung on Christmas morning will be selected from the collection recently compiled by Mr R. H. Heath, the organist. The chapel choir will be augmented by a full string band from the Redruth Orchestral Society. This innovation is certain to draw a large audience and advantage will be taken of this, making a collection for the choirs' expenses. In all probability Mr J. Herbert Williams will preside at the organ and Mr Heath will perform the duties of the conductor. Amongst the carols sung at the Free Church

will be three or four of the compositions of Mr M. Clemens, organist. Mr Hilton organist of the Bible Christian Chapel has also composed several carols and an anthem which will be sung by the choir during the Christmas services. The Primitive Methodist choir (Mr. Nicholas, organist) are also practicing assiduously and will doubtless give a good account of themselves.' (*West Briton*, December 26th 1889 – we think this article missed the Christmas deadline)

These hedge choirs were again mentioned in 1900 and show how the carols were not confined to the chapels but were being sung everywhere: 'No singing within walls can equal the beauty and sweetness of open air carolling, where the miners' powerful voices blend in thrilling harmony'. (Michael Tangye)

Composers

We have given some background in the following section of the book to the composers of the carols printed, such as Broad, Nicholas and Merritt. Many of these composers were self taught and a description of one – Joseph Pryor – was republished in *Old Cornwall* in 1943 from the *Western Daily Mercury* of 1890. It is entitled 'Joseph Pryor of Lanner: A Cornish Harmonious Blacksmith', and was written by Ashley Rowe:

> 'Mr Pryor was known, in all the country round to every carol-singer (and what Cornishman is not a carol singer?) as Joe Pryor … most of his life was spent in his native place. He was a blacksmith and a contemporary of Aaron Woolf, Thomas Broad and other writers of carols, whose works Mr Heath has incorporated in his very interesting little book of these Cornish hymns. For many years he was the leader of the choir at the Wesleyan Chapel in Lanner … Mr Pryor was an expert player on the 'cello and violin, and was acquainted with the mysteries of the serpent a wood-reed instrument not often seen in these days. He was a prolific composer of carols, anthems and hymn tunes, which were never published, but were handed about the neighbourhood in manuscript. Many of them are well known and at this time of year may be heard from the lips of numerous parties of glee singers in the inns or on the roads in the neighbourhood of Redruth of an evening … The tunes are all in the fugal style, so much loved by the Cornish people … Mr Pryor did not write on the ordinary staves, but recorded his ideas on paper by means of figures.'

A couple of other composers well known around that time but not featured in this book are worth mentioning too: Matthew Clemens (1866-1951), organist, choirmaster and conductor at the United Methodist Free Church in Redruth, known as the Flowerpot Chapel, where he began Christmas services at 5:45am. He has two of his carols published in Leese's collection (see section on Publications below). The other is William Eade, who died in 1864, a miner from Bucketts Hill, Redruth, who was connected with the Plain-An-Gwarry Primitive Methodist Chapel and had carols printed in Heath's volumes. It is clear that all these composers and musicians were known to each other and created a hotbed of musical inspiration.

Publications

Doidge's pocket books of carol words, 1889 and earlier

'Carol broadsides were formerly printed at Helston and hawked by pedlars just before Christmas at a half-penny. I have often seen them attached to walls of cottages in the neighbourhood of my home. They gave the words of the Cornish variants of the Mediaeval Carols: and as time went on they included such words as were available of the Redruth-Camborne carols. Later, these broadsides were replaced by small penny carol books published by Doidge of Redruth: and all prospective carol-singers had one of these in his pocket for several weeks before Christmas' (Dunstan).

In the *West Briton* and *Cornwall Advertiser* in December 1889 there is an advert which runs: 'Christmas Carols, One Penny. Per post 1½ d. F. Rodda, Publisher, Penzance' – this was another pocket book of just words obviously sold in Penzance. Alongside this advert there is one for a collection of *Cornish Carols* 'Now being published, 32 Old Cornish Carols composed by J. Stevens, J. Broad, W. Eade, A. Wolf and others. Arranged and adapted for mixed voices by R. H. Heath, Organist Redruth, to whom all orders must be sent. Church and Chapel choirs liberally dealt with'. This collection was the first of many which realised the significance of these carol hymns and is therefore of great importance to our canon of Cornish carols. In the preface to his collection he says:

> 'For some considerable time our Cornish friends at home and in the colonies have been clamouring for a collection of Cornish Carols … and seeing the tenacity with which the Cornish folk stick to the yearly rendering of these compositions as handed down from father to son, and not merely singing them in the chapels and churches but in the highways and hedges, I have thought for some years past that perhaps something might be done to still further perpetuate these rude compositions'.

Front cover of Heath's Cornish Carols, *from Tregajorran Chapel, 1889*

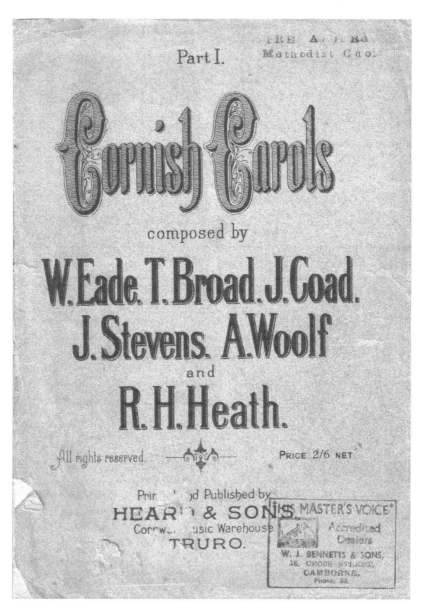

Many of the original scores were provided by Humphrey Broad who was the son of Thomas Broad and organist at the Primitive Methodist Chapel before Heath and who also taught Thomas Merritt.

Robert Hainsworth Heath (1842-1911) was born in the Torquay or Newton Abbott area of Devon, but moved to Cornwall where he was 'undoubtedly a very prominent figure in the musical life of Redruth … he had arrived in Redruth as a playing member of a circus band [and] he was a very accomplished cornet player'. He became a music teacher and organist at Plain-an-Gwarry Chapel and then for the Wesley Chapel, collecting and writing carols which he published in two volumes. He also published *Devonshire Carols*, collected and edited by R. H. Heath in 1895, and a number of other works both secular and religious. The Redruth Oratorio Society was formed by Heath in 1868. It became the Redruth Choral Society, which has continued into this millennium. He lived in the aptly named Harmony Cottage, which may have been in Coach Lane in Redruth. He and his wife, Redruth-born Mary Ann Heath, had eight children. 'Mr. Heath had decided by 1894 to leave the town and emigrate to South Africa... Robert Heath's departure from Redruth Station … was a very tearful farewell'. (Denzil Richards, *The Redruth Choral Society*, 2014)

A reprint of Heath's collection was made by R. Vigo of Falmouth. Although undated, we think it was published in the 1960s. In the introduction it says: 'On a recent buying trip, I purchased a quantity of Victorian Sheet Music. Amongst this music I came across parts of two pamphlets of Cornish Carols. These were originally published in 1889 by Mr R. H. Heath of Redruth. These two pamphlets were sold by Mackay Bros. Music House of Johannesburg. Obviously they were purchased by an exiled Cousin Jack and brought back home. As my own great-great Grandfather mined out in South Africa in the Witwatersrand, I took it upon myself to restore and republish those carols still in one piece. It is to those wonderful Cousin Jacks who left their homeland (and still do – as I had to) I respectfully dedicate this collection'.

Hot on the heels of Heath's publication came another from Redruth in 1892 by Joseph Leese (MA, Mus B, Cantab), entitled *Old Cornish Carols*. He succeeded Heath as organist and choirmaster at the Wesley Chapel in Redruth but was a Lancashire man educated at Cambridge. 'In 1892 about eighty men sang carols in the Arcade at the bottom of Fore Street, the majority of them bass singers … He would listen in semi-darkness, frantically writing down the music of these unpublished local traditional carols' (M. Tangye). It is fascinating that there is so little overlap between Heath's two volumes of sixty three carols and Leese's seventeen. However, Leese adds three carols from Davies Gilbert's collection of early carols including 'A Virgin Most Pure'. In his preface he writes:

> 'The majority of the Cornish Carols contained in this book have been selected from old MS collections handed to me for the purpose … The old carols are of interest as being not only genuine people's music but also people's part music, which is a much rarer thing. It is earnestly to be hoped that the Cornishmen will not allow the custom of carol singing to die out. It is much too good to perish! – Why not develope [sic] it?'

Leese left Cornwall in 1898 to work at Streatham Wesleyan Chapel in London where he introduced Thomas Merritt's carols. Merritt's carols were extremely popular in the early twentieth century, although none of his early manuscripts have survived. In the 1920s, however, two volumes of six of his carols were published by the Reid Brothers (who also printed Ralph Dunstan's *Carol Book*). They were reprinted later in 1977 as *Twelve Cornish Carols by Merritt* by Lodenek Press which became the Cornish Music Company.

Two other publications should be mentioned, especially that of Thomas Ninnes Warmington (1874-1955) from Carbis Bay, who remains to this day very well respected in West Cornwall for his collections of carols. He produced two volumes of forty carols entitled *A Selection of Old Christmas Carols and Anthems* in 1912. It is this collection that is used for many of the St Ives carols, such as 'Let Eastern Tribes', but his arrangements of 'Hark What Music', 'Seraphic Minstrels' and 'Star of Bethlehem' too are known in other parts of Cornwall. Unfortunately he does not assign any composers' names to the carols, except those he has written himself – and there is no preface.

One other collection, also called *Old Cornish Carols*, was published in 1927 and is of manuscripts from Tregony, printed in Polperro and edited by B. Barnicoat. He says in his preface:

> 'This selection of Old Cornish Carols is transcribed from manuscripts written and collected by my Grandfather, the late Francis Woolcock, who was born in Tregoney [*sic*] in 1810 and died in the same place in 1888. The manuscripts now in my possession are only a part of my late Grandfather's extensive collection of old music and are probably copies of earlier manuscripts, in use in the early part of the eighteenth century. I often heard my Grandfather speak of them as "tunes" and "pieces" sung and played in the days of Wesley. In transcribing for present day use, every care has been taken to preserve the original harmonies, and only in isolated instances (where perhaps the manuscript is not quite clear) has any possible departure been made. The composers save in two or three instances are unknown.'

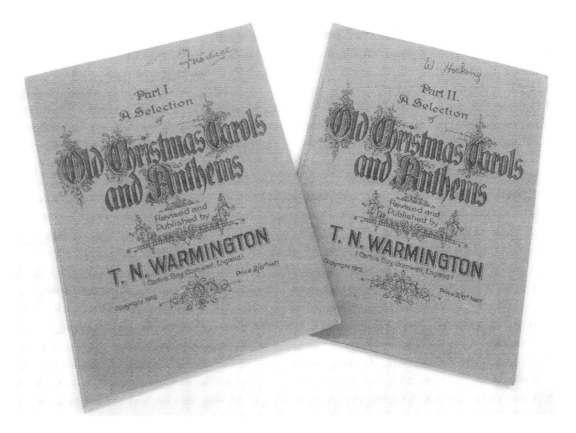

In the *Western Morning News* of 1925 there is an article from 'Our London Correspondent' entitled 'A Musical Farmworker's Collection', about Francis Woolcock. He was 'a musical land worker. He had a reputation locally as a musician but he had no education in the sense of the term as it is understood today … He obviously played the bassoon and most of the written music, which he copied in his notebook was written for the curious old wind instruments which were so popular with rustic musicians in those days. The earliest date of Woolcock's notebook is given on the flyleaf in an indistinct inscription which reads like "Richard Paull's book 1825".'

In a later edition of the *Western Morning News* there is a reply by Charles Beard of Perranwell, who lived formerly in Tregony:

> 'As Tregoney [sic] People we have always been proud of our Christmas carols although we had no written music of them. They came to us by heir ship, our fathers taught us and their fathers taught them. The present generation seems to be nearly as well-versed in the rendering as we considered we were in our time'.

There are several overlaps with the Redruth carols, for example 'Seraphic Minstrels', but many of the carols are distinct. Sadly, we did not hear these on our travels.

Above: Warmington's two volumes of Cornish carols, 1912

Opposite: Ralph Dunstan, carol and folk song collector and arranger, 1919

The Angels' Song (Glory, Glory)

On 'the first Thursday before the last Thursday before Christmas' in December 2015 we went to the Picrous Eve celebrations at the Kings Arms at Luxulyan, where we recorded this carol. This is an event we've been to many times over a number of years, and it is always a good occasion. It was resurrected quite a few years ago (how many exactly seems to be lost in a piskie-led haze) by Hilary's brother, Will Coleman, who told us:

'We had a crew of singers based around Lanlivery – "we have no name, but we do have a repu-tation" as John Kift always said. I had always known about Picrous Night from reading Robert Hunt and it just seemed too good an under-our-noses opportunity to miss up. The landlord at 'Bridges' (aka Kings Arms) in those days was Kenny Saundry, and he was always ready to delight the assembled company with a yarn and a joke. At its height the pub used to be rammed with hun-dreds of merry-makers and every year something wacky and unusual would kick off. The best of all was when a group of Rajasthani bagpipers, drummers and dancers visiting Eden all called in – we had the best multicultural version of The White Rose you ever heard! We first learned the song "Glory, Glory", or as we called it "The Angels' Song", from singers such as Rusty Eplett, Robert Grose and Nick Nicholls of Fowey. They always said it was a "Golant Song" and we never argued – neither did the Golant crew of Micky Morgan, Vic Tabb and Penny Parsons. I remember Rob Grose Sr telling me that the technique to get the proper full-bore sound "you have to sing from your heart to yer throat"'.

In *Biglow & Main's Christmas Annual*, produced in New York in 1877, we see the first publication of this carol, under the name 'The Angel's Song', where it is attributed to Robert Lowry. It is found in many hymnals published between then and the 1920s, including Ira Sankey's *Sacred Songs and Solos*, 1890. Sankey hymns became very popular in Cornwall and that perhaps accounts for it being well known here. The original ver-sion is written in Ab major, but interestingly Sankey's version is in Eb major, which is the key most people in Cornwall seem to sing it in. The many versions in print come under various titles including 'Glory, Glory', 'The Angel Song', 'Glory In The Highest', and 'Rolling Downwards', but they all have the same arrangement, the only difference being in the earlier versions where the third line of the third verse was originally: 'Man of sorrows, and rejected', rather than 'Child of Mary, Man of Sorrows', as is more commonly sung today.

Robert Lowry (1826-1899), American composer of hymns and carols

Robert Wadsworth Lowry (1826-1899) was born in Philadelphia, Pennsylvania, USA and as a child he was very fond of music, playing a variety of musical instruments. Later he became a Baptist minister, as well as working for a time at the Biglow Publishing Company as a music editor. He composed around five hundred hymns and pieces of gospel music, including 'Shall We Gather at the River'.

Today across Cornwall, and wherever in the world Cornishmen are found, 5 March is celebrated as St Piran's Day. St Piran, one of Cornwall's three patron saints along

Singers at Picrous Eve, King's Arms, Luxulyan, 2016

with St Michael and St Petroc, is considered to be the discoverer of tin. However in mid-Cornwall that honour is given to a man known as Picrous. According to Robert Hunt in his *Popular Romances of the West of England*, 1865, 'The second Thursday before Christmas-day is a festival observed by the tinners of the district of Blackmore, and known as Picrous day … it is the occasion of a supper and much merry-making. The owner of the tin-stream contributes a shilling a man towards it. This is said to be the feast of the discovery of tin by a man named Picrous … Picrous day is believed to have been especially popular in Luxulyan.'

In West Cornwall the tin miners used to celebrate Chewidden Day or Chewidden Thursday. This festival celebrated the discovery of tin smelting, and Hunt tells us that 'The last Thursday – a clear week before Christmas Day – was formerly always claimed by the tinners as a holiday, and was called by them White-Thursday (*Jew-whidn*), because on this day, according to tradition, black tin (tin ore) was first smelted and refined into white tin'. The word Chewidden may come from the late Cornish, *Jew-*

whidn, as Hunt says, or from *Chy Widn*, meaning white house which is a term for a smelting house.

So at Luxulyan we were welcomed, as always, by our old friends from that area and others from further east, the singers' ages spanning over fifty years. Gathering round the covered pool table we soon got going with Nick Nicholls leading off many of the carols, pausing only to eat the pasties provided for us by the landlord, Stephen Lewis, while he regaled us with the legend of Jan Sturtridge, retold from Hunt's book, which is a tale of being piskie-led.

'One Picrous Night John Sturtridge, who, well primed with ale, started on his homeward way for Luxulyan Church-town. John had got as far as Tregarden Down without any mishap worth recording, when, alas! he happed upon a party of the little people, who were at their sports in the shelter of a huge granite boulder. Assailed by shouts of derisive laughter, he hastened on frightened and bewildered, but the Down, well known from early experience, became like ground untrodden, and after long trial no gate or stile was to be found. He was getting vexed, as well as puzzled, when a chorus of tiny voices shouted: "Ho! and away for Par Beach!" John repeated the shout, and was in an instant caught up, and in a twinkling found himself on the sands of Par. A brief dance, and the cry was given: "Ho! and away for Squire Tremain's cellar!" A repetition of the Piskie cry found John with his elfish companions in the cellars at Heligan, where was beer and wine galore. It need not be said that he availed himself of his opportunities. The mixture of all the good liquors so affected him that, alas! he forgot in time to catch up the next cry of "Ho! and away for Par Beach!" In the morning John was found by the butler, groping and tumbling among butts and barrels, very much muddled with the squire's good drink. His strange story, very incoherently told, was not credited by the squire, who committed him to jail for the burglary, and in due time he was convicted and sentenced to death. The morning of his execution arrived; a large crowd had assembled, and John was standing under the gallows tree, when a commotion was observed in the crowd, and a little lady of commanding mien made her way through the opening throng to the scaffold. In a shrill, sweet voice, which John recognised, she cried: "Ho! and away for France!" which being replied to, he was rapt from the officers of justice, leaving them and the multitude mute with wonder and disappointment'. (Robert Hunt, *Romances of the West of England*, 1865).

The Angels' Song (Glory, Glory) R. LOWRY (1826-99)

CD 1 Track 7

1.Roll - ing down - ward thro' the mid - night, Comes a
2.Won - d'ring shep - herds see the glo - ry, Hear the
3.Christ the Sa - viour, God's A - noint - ed, Comes to

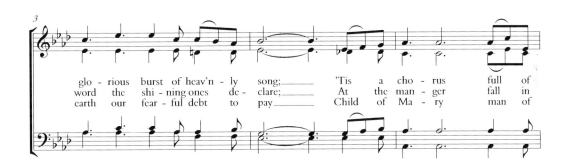

glo - rious burst of heav'n - ly song;____ 'Tis a cho - rus full of
word the shi - ning ones de - clare;____ At the man - ger fall in
earth our fear - ful debt to pay____ Child of Ma - ry man of

sweet - ness And the sing - ers are an an - gel throng.____
wor - ship, While the mu - sic fills the quiv' - ring air.____ 'Glo - ry!
sor - rows, Lamb of God, that takes our sins a - way.____

Glo - ry in the high - est! On the earth good will and peace to men!'__ Down the
Glo - ry! Glo - ry! Glo - ry!

a - ges
a - ges, down the a - ges   send the e - cho;   Let the glad earth shout_ a - gain!_

The Angels' Song (Glory, Glory)
As sung at Picrous Eve, Luxulyan, December 2016

1. Rolling downwards through the midnight
Comes a glorious burst of heavenly song
Tis a chorus full of sweetness
And the singers are an angel throng.

Chorus
Glory Glory in the highest
On the earth good will and peace to men
Down the ages send the echo
Let the glad earth shout again!

2. Wond'ring shepherds see the glory
Hear the words the shining ones declare
At the manger fall in worship
While the music fills the quivering air.

3. Christ the Saviour, God's Anointed
Comes to earth our fearful debt to pay
Child of Mary, Man of Sorrows
Son of God that takes our sins away.

Awake Ye Nations (Wakey, Wakey)

This is a carol by Thomas Broad, who has been described as the 'father of the Cornish carol'. He shaped a pattern, created a style, and set a trend' (K. Pelmear, *Carols of Cornwall*, 1982). He was a composer from Broad Lane, Illogan, and choirmaster at Harris Mill Chapel. He was also a miner who became a mine manager in Cuba and died there of a fever 1848.

Tregajorran Chapel Choir, 1947

Thomas' son, Humphrey Broad, became choirmaster at Plain-an-Gwarry chapel in Redruth and supplied Heath with manuscripts for his publication in 1889. Humphrey Broad also taught Thomas Merritt.

It is likely that 'Awake Ye Nations' would have been composed in the early 1800s, and we assume Broad wrote both music and lyrics. Its first publication seems to have been in Heath's *Cornish Carol* collection of 1889. However, the words were printed by Richard Woolcock on at least two broadsides between 1844 and 1881.

It was also one of the first carols learnt by the Tregajorran Singers, who sing it on our recording. This was because of a local oral history project Hilary undertook in 1999 when she interviewed Pam Curnow, who had lived in Tregajorran all her life. Pam gave her Heath's book and said she remembered that particular one sung at the Tregajorran Chapel by the choir in the 1940s. Another memory of around that time came from Henry Eva, who sang in the choir: '*One Christmas the first car in Tregajorran (owned by the Pooleys) made a trip to the pub. The car was full of men off for a song. On returning, and after a few drinks, the car ended up in a ditch. Unperturbed the men got out and carried on singing in Tregajorran square even though their wives came out and begged them to come in for Christmas dinner!*'

*Moonta poster
illustrated by
Oswald Pryor*

He told us the square was always a meeting place for singers, and they would then sing around the village, Carn Brea, Treskillard and Piece with the 'couple in love always singing out of position!' And so since 1998, the Treggy Singers have always gathered at the square on Christmas Eve to sing: *'On Christmas Eve we had our own Tregajorran carols. The singers arrived at our house about 6.30pm and it was lovely to hear 'Hark the Glad Sound' getting louder as they entered the house – it felt like Christmas had begun! We then sang walking down the hill; the first line of 'Glory Glory' – 'Rolling Downward' seemed very appropriate, going to others' houses and meeting with more singers until we arrived at the square – lovely! I recorded 'Awake Ye Nations' and other carols there'. (H. Coleman, 2015)*

The carol seems to have been a favourite at the Redruth Flowerpot Chapel in Victorian times; it was sung there at the Christmas services of 1875 to 1880 before other carols took its place.

Joseph Leese's *Old Cornish Carols* also has 'Awake Ye Nations' with no composer but essentially it is the same as Broad's except with a few variations in the parts – for example the tenors start the canon rather than the sopranos.

Another version altogether is in Barnicoat's collection, and yet another two versions are found in Dunstan's publication, one of which he attributes both words and music to Moyle from Chacewater and the other is set to a tune named Cornwall.

However, Broad's version does feature in the second edition of *The Christmas Welcome*, a Cornish Carol collection from Moonta, Australia, 1893. So it must have remained popular with the Cornish overseas. This version also has the tenors beginning the canon. There is a curious connection with Hilary's parents: *'In 1997, on an extended visit to Australia, we spent three days in the part of South Australia known as Little Cornwall. We stayed in a bed and breakfast in the middle of the Moonta Mines Heritage Site, with the huge red tailing heaps (tips) within a stone's throw. We visited Moonta Cemetery and found many gravestones carved with Cornish names and places. The latter included St Just, Gwennap, Redruth and Ludgvan. Having mentioned in a junk shop in Kadina that we were interested in Cornish music, we were directed back to Moonta to visit a couple who lived in the rear part of an old Methodist chapel. The main part of the building was a treasure-trove of all things discarded. We spent some time searching through piles of sheet music, and came across an unfamiliar setting of the 'Soldier's Farewell' and pages 17 to 34 of a book of Cornish carols! We asked for these pages to be photocopied for us.*

The carols included some written or arranged by L. Davey, J. H. Thomas, J. Glasson and T. Broad. The one by T. Broad (from Illogan) was called 'Awake Ye Nations of the Earth' and, on returning home, we asked Ian Marshall to arrange it for the Calstock Singers. The Singers christened it 'Wakey, Wakey' (to match 'Glory, Glory' and 'Harky, Harky'!) and it became a great favourite'(Marion Coleman).

So this carol was being revived at two ends of Cornwall, within Hilary's family each initially unaware of that fact!

Awake Ye Nations (Wakey, Wakey) THOMAS BROAD (? -1848)

CD 1 Track 8

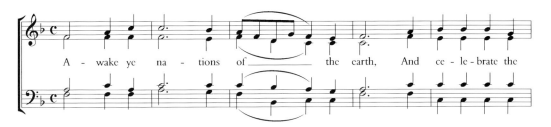

A - wake ye na - tions of the earth, And ce - le - brate the

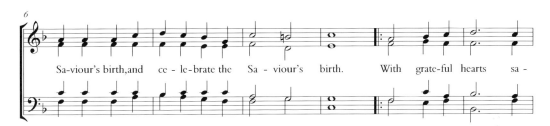

Sa-viour's birth, and ce - le-brate the Sa - viour's birth. With grate-ful hearts sa -

On which the Sa-viour Christ was born, on which the Sa - viour

-lute the morn On which the Sa - viour Christ was born, on

On which the Sa - viour

Christ was born,

which the Sa-viour Christ was born, on which the Sa - viour Christ was born.

Christ was born,

Awake Ye Nations (Wakey, Wakey)
As sung at Tregajorran Square, Christmas Eve, 2015

1. Awake ye nations of the earth
And celebrate the Saviour's birth
With grateful hearts salute the morn
On which the Saviour, Christ was born.

2. The shining hosts on wings of love
Flew swiftly from the courts above
With acclamations from the skies
And seized the shepherds with surprise.

3. The heav'nly choir around did sing
This day is born the Saviour King
They swell their notes of praise again
Glory to God, goodwill to men.

Calm on the Listening Ear of Night

In 1984, Philip Payton wrote *Cornish Carols from Australia*, which contains carols reproduced from a collection from 1893, entitled *A Christmas Welcome: A Choice Collection of Cornish Carols* and published in Moonta, South Australia. This carol is included, composed by J. H. Thomas.

The rise of popularity in the Cornish carol during the years 1850 to 1900 also coincided with the Great Migration: the crashes of the copper and tin mining industries in Cornwall (1860s and 70s) combined with the agricultural depression in the 1870s and the decline of the fishing industry resulted in a huge Cornish emigration. Censuses from that period show that over a quarter of a million people left Cornwall to find work around the world but most notably in South Africa, America and Australia.

South Australia became a principal destination for Cousin Jacks due to the mineral wealth there and the assisted passage scheme, ending in 1886, meant that a steady flow of Cornish men and women to the area kept their cultural roots strong. Cornish communities grew around the first mines, and the townships of Wallaroo, Moonta and Kadina became known as Little Cornwall. The Cornish carols were a meeting point for two strong elements of the Cornish inheritance: music-making and Methodism. Obviously, the Cornish people took their carols with them but, as in Cornwall during this period, there emerged a number of talented carol composers amongst the Australian Cornish. So although *A Christmas Welcome* did have some old favourites from Cornwall the majority of songs were newly composed in Australia, in the same style. There were nine contributors to the collection including a J. Coad (who could well be the composer from Illogan included in Heath's collection) and J. H. 'Johnnie' Thomas.

Left: Cornish carol books from Australia, 1893 and 1920s

Below: Australian cartoonist Oswald Pryor's sketch of Cornish carol composer Johnny Thomas, early 20th century

Oswald Pryor, an Australian born of Cornish parentage, was a cartoonist from 1901 onwards. He wrote a history of Australia's Little Cornwall and implies that it was Thomas who edited the collection. He also created a wonderful sketch of Johnnie Thomas 'depicting him as a sprightly, impish little man, brimming over with enthusiasm and energy. Pryor's cartoons had a reputation for being extraordinarily true-to-life, his sketches capturing not only the physical characteristics but the personality as well' (Payton).

Researcher Kate Neale has been in touch with J. H. Thomas' family, who still live in Australia. They told her that 'Calm on the Listening Ear of Night' is still performed in church services there describing it as a Moonta classic.

> 'Without fear of over exaggeration, one could venture to suggest that James Richards and Johnnie Thomas together were Australia's answer to Cornwall's Thomas Merritt' (Payton).

Edmund Hamilton Sears (1810-1876), lyricist

The words were written by Edmund Hamilton Sears (1810-1876) who is perhaps better known for writing 'It Came Upon a Midnight Clear'. Sears was an American Unitarian parish minister. He is an interesting man who preached the equality of women and men, and was a staunch abolitionist. The carol is found in Chope's collection of 1894 set to a tune he describes as Devonshire.

One evening in December 2015 we set off for Pencarrow House near Wadebridge to record the Washaway West Gallery Choir. Pencarrow is a Georgian house, still privately owned by the Molesworth St Aubyn family, and interestingly, during our research, we discovered a link between this family and the Padstow carol 'Rouse, Rouse'. At Pencarrow we met Peter Meanwell, the choir's MD, who has a huge knowledge of Cornish carols and was kind enough to help with the scores for this book. The choir sang a wide range of carols from across Cornwall, but we decided to feature this one as it has a lovely connection to the Cornish diaspora and Australia, as well as being a beautiful carol in its own right.

Peter Meanwell has a long connection with singing sacred music, having sung with the York Minster Cathedral Choir for ten years. He didn't have his own choir until he started the Washaway West Gallery Choir around 2000, specifically to sing West Gallery music. Peter says his interest in this style of singing came from his Methodist upbringing when they sang hymns of this type.

Peter's interest in the old Cornish carols had been sparked in the 1990s *'when I heard Gloria Dinnis, the organist at Week St Mary chapel, play Hark the Glad Sound at the end of a carol service. Gloria told me that it was from a book that her father had written down – Christmas Carols, Old, copied by Stephen Jose in 1927, and was from St Gennys'*. This was one of the carols we heard the choir sing at Pencarrow which differed from the two versions in this book.

Peter and the Washaway Choir did the first of their now annual Christmas concerts at Pencarrow in 2001 or 2002, after which he started researching Cornish carols. Their repertoire now includes a variety of carols that he has found in old manuscripts and books.

Peter was prompted to sing this particular carol with his choir after a meeting with Kate Neale.

We also heard the choir sing 'What Melody is This I Hear', also by J. H. Thomas. Peter combined the version published in *The Christmas Welcome*, with the version in Thomas Banfield's MS book from St Ives.

Calm on the Listening Ear of Night J. H. THOMAS, words EDMUND HAMILTON SEARS (1810-1876)

CD 1 Track 9

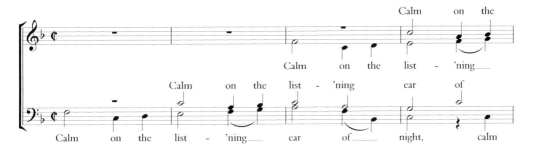

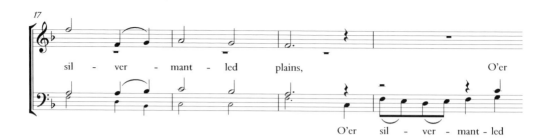

sil - ver - mant - led plains, O'er

O'er sil - ver - mant - led

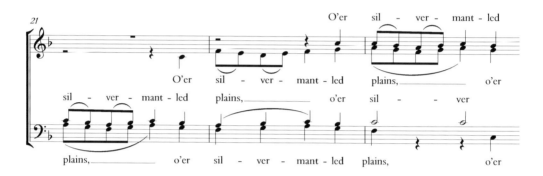

O'er sil - ver - mant - led

O'er sil - ver - mant - led plains, o'er

sil - ver - mant - led plains, o'er sil - ver

plains, o'er sil - ver - mant - led plains, o'er

plains,

sil - ver - mant - led plains, o'er sil - ver - mant - led plains.

mant - led plains,

sil - ver mant - led plains,

As sung by the Washaway West Gallery Choir at Pencarrow House, December 2015

1. Calm on the listening ear of night
Came heav'n's melodious strains;
Where wide Judea stretches far
O'er silver mantled plains.

2. Celestial choirs from courts above
Shed sacred glory there;
And angels with their sparkling lyres
Made music in the air.

3. Glory to God the sounding skies
Loud with their anthems ring;
Peace to the earth, goodwill to men
From heav'n's eternal King.

Flaming Seraphs (The Stratton Carol)

'Flaming Seraphs', also known as the 'Stratton Carol', is probably the best known carol from the Bude-Stratton area of North Cornwall. The names of the writers of both words and music have been lost in the mists of time. However, the carol does appear in Chope's *Anthology of Christmas Carols* (1875), although in a slightly different form. Chope describes it as both Cornish and traditional, and his version was arranged by Herbert Stephen Irons.

This most widely sung of all the Stratton Carols was printed in the 1928 publication of the *Tre Pol and Pen* journal. Ralph Dunstan, then published it in his *Cornish Song Book* where he says that, according to Mrs Edith Jewell of Holsworthy, this carol was sung in Stratton during her youth, and was known as the 'Stratton Carol'. He also tells us that 'so far as our fathers and grandfathers can recollect', it has been sung at Stratton from time immemorial. He collected the melody and bass from Mr W. Cowling who lived in Bolingey but could have come from North Cornwall.

The Bude, Stratton and District Old Cornwall Society published *Carols of the Stratton Hundred, North Cornwall* for their 50th anniversary in 2011, and it won a Holyer an Gof Award from the Cornish Gorsedd. This book contains forty carols, including 'Flaming Seraphs', all traditionally sung in this area and arranged by Michael Richardson. 'Flaming Seraphs' can also be found in Terry Bale's booklet *North Cornwall Carols*, printed in the early 2000s. This useful little book contains fourteen carols which Bale collected in that area. Some of these were arranged specifically for the book also by Michael Richardson and were rehearsed at Tremayna Chapel for a Christmas Concert broadcast by Radio Cornwall in 2000 and 2001. Bale tells us *All these carols have been sung in various village churches and chapels somewhere within Cornwall for as long as can be remembered'.*

On the evening of November 28th 2016, having been invited by Audrey Aylmer, of the Bude, Stratton and District Old Cornwall Society, we drove to the Parkhouse Centre in Bude for their annual carol concert, to hear the carols local to this area. This evening is devoted to encouraging the singing of these old carols, which were once sung around the farms and villages of the area at Christmas. The carols, popular here so many years ago, have been successfully revived by the Old Cornwall Society. The key figure in this revival has been Michael Richardson, who not only collected the carols from people in the surrounding villages but also transcribed and arranged many of them. We were very glad to meet him that night and talk to him. He told us that the choir was put together specifically to sing these carols, and that some of the singers have been involved in supporting this revival for several years.

As Audrey Aylmer explains: *'It is not a concert, the whole idea is to get everyone to join in the singing! Each year our Bude, Stratton and District Old Cornwall Society have an evening to sing the local traditional carols to keep them alive. Other Old Cornwall Societies throughout Cornwall also do this, our motto being "Gather the fragments lest they be lost". Most societies do it round the streets as it would have been done in times gone by … Michael researched a lot of the carols and started to include them at Christmas in Kilkhampton several years ago. Andrew Jewell then presented our society with a copy of the carols sung in his family. His Mother, Ethel Jewell, was a founder member of our OCS and our first President. She wrote firsthand accounts of Stratton life and events which Andrew collected and printed as* A Stratton Childhood.*'* Presumably, there

Bude and Stratton Old Cornwall Society singers with Mike Richardson (seated)

Bude and Stratton Old Cornwall Society banner

is a family connection between these Jewells and the Edith Jewell that Dunstan refers to.

There were copies of the *Carols of the Stratton Hundred,* available to buy, or just to borrow for the evening thus encouraging the audience to join in. The evening included singing the 'St Day Carol' and 'Hark the Glad Sound' in Cornish, the words for which were, once again, provided for the audience to participate. It was with some surprise that we heard 'Hark the Glad Sound' sung to something other than Merritt's well known tune. The fact of how little all these carols overlap with those we had heard in other parts of Cornwall, demonstrated to us the geographical separation between North Cornwall and the rest of the Duchy. Robert Heath also published a collection of *Devonshire Carols* after his two volumes, *Cornish Carols*. Some of the carols in that collection were also sung in North Cornwall. Heath says that many of them were sung in Lifton Parish Church which is just over the border in Devon.

Flaming Seraphs (The Stratton Carol) TRADITIONAL arr. Michael Richardson

CD 1 Track 10

Flaming Seraphs (The Stratton Carol)

As sung by the Bude and Stratton Old Cornwall Society Singers at the Parkhouse Centre, Bude, 2016

1. Hark! The music of the Cherubs
Bursting solemn through the sky!
And the band of flaming Seraphs
Telling wonders from on high!

2. See affrighted shepherds gazing
On that bright celestial host!
While the dazzling light is blazing
And they lie in wonder lost.

3. 'Cease your fears – a joyful story –
Unto you is born a child
Lo, He comes, the King of Glory
God to man is reconciled.

4. 'Yea, He leaves His blissful station
And descends with man to dwell
Robes himself with incarnation
And subdues the power of hell.'

5. Glory be to God the Father
Glory be to God the Son
Glory to the Spirit ever
The eternal Three in One.

Hail, Sacred Day, Auspicious Morn

'A thousand monuments of the great mining generation are now destroyed or decaying, but the notes of Thomas Merritt's music, rising to new climax each Christmas, continue to enshrine the ancient Christmas and Celtic spirit of Cornwall'. Introduction to the publication *Twelve Cornish Carols by Merritt.*

For more on Merritt himself see 'Hark the Glad Sound'. It is important to note that for many in Cornwall and its diaspora the Merritt carols continue to embody the spirit of Christmas. The above Lodenek Press publication, often known as Merritt's Twelve (these are the only carols of his known to have survived), was a reprint of an earlier two book set of six carols each, which have no date but were printed by Reid Brothers of London. They also have adverts for Dunstan's songbooks which date them around the late 1920s. However they are most likely also a reprint of earlier copies that have not survived. 'Hail, Sacred Day' is one of the carols in the first set; it is a beautifully written carol-hymn where the music really reflects the sentiments of the words.

The words seem to be a development from other carols known in Cornwall previously; William Sandys collected a carol, 'Hail Ever Hail the Auspicious Morn' and it is found again with a tune by Thomas Broad in Heath's collection. However the first line is really the only similarity. There are echoes too of Wesley's hymns: 'Arise my Soul Arise' and 'Hail the Day that Sees Him Rise', and it is clear that Merritt, with this and his other carols, was continuing a long tradition of devotional and uplifting hymn writing. Warmington also composed a version of 'Hail, Sacred Day'. Both he and Merritt could have been inspired by older manu-

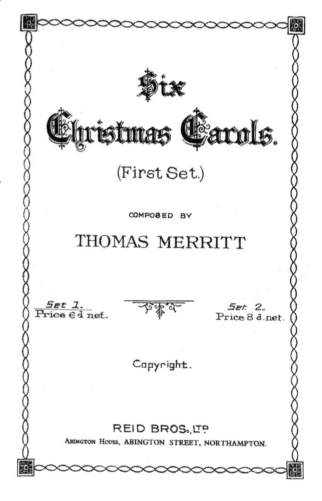

scripts, as in 'Hark the Glad Sound'.

Merritt's words are first found in *A Selection of Carols, Pieces, and Anthems, Suitable for Christmas*, a pocket book of words printed by F. Rodda from Penzance which, according to John Speller on his Cornish Carols website, was printed in 1870. This tallies with what we know of Merritt's compositions; his earliest pieces dating from the 1880s were printed at his own expense but later varying publishers printed his work. In an introduction to Merritt's recently discovered cantata, 'The Shepherd of Israel', which was published by Cowethas Ylow Kernewek in 1988, Jory Bennett states: '4000 copies of the first set of carols were sold during the Christmas season of 1899 alone and 600 of the second which had only just been issued'. An astonishing number!

These carols of Merritt's were hugely popular overseas as well as at home, particularly in America. In California, 'by the 1860s miners were singing for their own entertainment in carol clubs which gathered in the breweries and the bars … In 1876 John Ferrell, a miner and merchant, organised a carol choir at the Methodist church that became … the Grass Valley Carol Choir' (G. McKinney, CD sleeve notes, *When Miners Sang*, 2001).

Left: Augmented Choir inside Paynters Lane End Chapel, 2016

Opposite: Front cover of Merritt's carols, 1920s

Paynters Lane End chapel, 2017

By 1906 the Grass Valley Choir had so many singers that W. M. Argall organised a second group known as the Thomas Merritt Choir. These choirs reunited after the First World War and were broadcast many times on regional stations, luckily one of these recordings survived: the 1946 NBC National Broadcast, where they sing ten carols including 'Hail Sacred Day', 'Seraphic Minstrels', 'Star of Bethlehem' and 'Hark What Music'. The choir still exists today and a book about them and other Cornish choirs in America was published in 2001, called *When Miners Sang: the Grass Valley Carol Choir* by Gage McKinney.

This carol was also recorded as being sung by the Cornish singers of Painesdale Methodist Church in Michigan in 1949 with a note that the singers had never seen the song in print and had learnt it 'by rote and sung from memory'. They were also recorded singing four other Cornish carols including another Merritt – 'Lo He Comes an Infant Stranger'.

We recorded the carol one Sunday afternoon at the end of November 2016 when we visited Paynters Lane End Chapel, built in 1890, for their annual Merritt carol service. It is a beautiful chapel and very prominent, sitting on the five-ways crossing in the heart of Illogan. We were really pleased that we heard about this concert at the last minute because we had hoped we could record at least one Merritt carol in the place he had lived. Merritt was born in 1863 at Broad Lane, Illogan, and baptised at the chapel there. He lies buried just a short distance away in the churchyard. As an adult, he played the organ in many chapels around Illogan: the Bible Christian Chapel in Chili Road from the age of twenty two; the United Methodist Free Church on Illogan Highway from 1889, when he was twenty-six; and Illogan Wesleyan Church from the age of thirty-eight, in 1901. He also conducted a small orchestra at nearby Voguebeloth Wesleyan Sunday School.

The service was informal and funny with an augmented choir, made up of singers from Redruth Methodist, Stithians Ladies, Holmans Climax and Four Lanes Male Voice Choirs. There was no conductor and it was a testament to how embedded these carols are in the community that none was needed. It was quite a short service and three of Merritt's carols were sung, as well as Nicholas' 'Star of Jacob'. These were 'Hark the Glad Sound', 'Hail, Sacred Day' and 'Come Let Us All with One Accord'.

The minister was Stella Rule who, now 86 years old, remembered carol singing around Illogan for many years: *We went carol singing round Illogan every year. We were raising funds for a different charity. We used to go out back in the fifties, lanterns, torches, on a starlit night, wonderful! I've been connected with the Paynters Lane End Chapel all my life. My Great Grandmother brought me when I was three, and I've been here ever since! Get to January, that'll be eighty-four years.'*

She told us that when they used to go carol singing the leader would always leave 'Hail, Sacred Day' to the end and would then finally say 'Let's have Suspicious Morn!'

Hail, Sacred Day, Auspicious Morn
As sung by an augmented choir at Paynters Lane End Chapel, Illogan November 2016

1. Hail, sacred day, auspicious morn
On which the Prince of Life was born!
Messiah leaves His Father's throne
The Glorious Lord of Life comes down.

2. Arise, my soul, and hail the day
Nor sleep the solemn hours away
Let heavenly hosts arise and sing
Hosannas to the new-born King!

3. Peace now resumes her gentle reign
Good-will and love are given to men
Thus sang the bright angelic host
While shepherds were in wonder lost.

4. Glory to God who reigns on high!
Proclaim glad tidings through the sky
Let heaven and earth salute the morn
On which the Prince of Life was born.

Hail Sacred Day, Auspicious Morn THOMAS MERRITT (1863-1908)

CD 1 Track 11

Hark the Glad Sound (Merritt)

'In my opinion, Merritt was the king of Cornish carols'. (Roy Thomas, Troon Toc H)

To us 'Hark the Glad Sound' only means one thing – Merritt's superb carol! Yet when we started our research we discovered that the words, written by Phillip Dodderidge in 1735, had been set to many other tunes around Cornwall, such as at Port Isaac, and also in other parts of Britain.

Yet again as in 'Hail, Sacred Day', Merritt seems to have been inspired by these older texts. Merritt gave a newspaper interview in the *Cornish Post and Mining News*, 1900, in which he says: 'Music is meat and drink to me: and whatever I have done has been mainly by patient study and hard work. When a boy I used to delight in whistling airs of my own composition, and at nine years of age I sang in a choir; and I am indebted to one or two friends for the foundation upon which I have built'.

He said that both sides of the family 'were intensely music loving though musically-illiterate'. He was born in 1863, the son of miner, becoming a miner himself until ill health caused him to retire at the age of 18 to become a music teacher.

He was taught by Humphrey Broad of Redruth, who was Thomas Broad's son and

Harmony Choir conductor, Ivor Richardson and Hilary Coleman, 2016

Thomas Merritt (1863-1908), composer and musician

organist at the Plain-an-Gwarry chapel in Redruth. The *Cornish Post* records: 'He does all his compositions on paper after committing the words to memory and studying light and shade, feeling and metaphors in the verses'.

In 1907 Merritt was diagnosed as suffering from consumption. He deteriorated rapidly and for the last two months of his life was confined to bed unable to work. He died on Good Friday, 17th April, 1908, aged 44. Merritt 'saw his role as a composer was to provide music which people could sing and enjoy – bright simple music which spoke eloquently and fell easily on the ears'. (Geoffrey Baggs, *Western Morning News*, 1968)

In the introduction to *The Shepherd of Israel*, 1988, Malcolm Arnold, who was interested in Merritt's work, says: 'Thomas Merritt was able to overcome such wretched material circumstances and give us some of the most vigorous and joyous music it has been my pleasure to hear' and Jory Bennett added: *'The same power which brought it into being had enjoined John Wesley to preach and Billy Bray to dance'.*

On Christmas Eve 2016 we went to Falmouth to hear the Harmony Choir sing through the streets many Cornish carol favourites including Merritt's 'Hark the Glad Sound'. They met at the Falmouth Watersports centre at 9am then had a quick practice (their only one of the year) before winding their way through Falmouth to the Moor and the Seven Stars pub. The choir was founded in 1900 as the Falmouth Docks Foundry Choir to raise money for the sick and unemployed members of the Docks' workforce at Christmas. Nowadays it is made up of members of local male voice choirs and raises money for good causes in Falmouth.

Their current conductor, Ivor 'Raffy' Richardson says: *'We rely on people coming to us. I've just spoken to a chap who's come from Sennen, and down Marazion, Mousehole, from Mevagissey, Newquay, and they just come and keep this tradition going. Originally it was down the docks area and they never used to come up through the town, until the late 1920s. They used to collect within the docks for those who were unfortunate enough to be unemployed or sick. My Dad and family used to work down the docks in the 1900s. I served my time down there as an apprentice, that was in 1946. In the 1940s, they used to have a ready-made choir in the docks because a lot of people used to come in from Camborne, Redruth and around, to work. They used to practice about two weeks before in the lunch hour in the joiner's shop, that's where I was apprentice – the joiner's shop. The conductor then, Harry Owens, was pattern maker down there.'*

Kevin Gerry, the secretary went on to say that: *'This Christmas will be the choir's 117th performance and even two world wars didn't stop us! Our conductor Ivor 'Raffy' Richardson was shadowed this year by Rob Norman* (from the Falmouth singers The Oggymen) *who will start to share in the conducting of the choir. Ivor is not laying down his baton just yet and will continue conducting the choir for the foreseeable future. Rob will only be the fifth person to conduct the choir'.*

Elaine Holman, who lived in Falmouth in the 1950s, says: *'You took your life in your*

hands if you were walking in the main street as all the men, maybe a thousand, used to come pouring out of the dock gates and along the road, some of them running and some pushing bikes. Not many people had cars in those days and also the main street was two-way. We used to squash ourselves against the wall to prevent ourselves being knocked over! Quite a daily sight. However, at Christmas when the men came from work some of them would gather and sing carols. I think this is where I first heard "Lyngham" in all its glory. I can remember listening to them when they were standing in the open area that used to be in front of the Odeon Cinema. This was on the same side of the road as the present Seasalt shop but on the opposite corner'.

Harmony Choir and crowd, Falmouth, December 2016

By all accounts Merritt was a prolific composer of music and song but much of this work has been lost. However we are very grateful that his Twelve Carols have survived for us to sing today. When interviewing Rick Williams, from Newlyn, he said:

'I always feel compelled to share my thoughts on Merritt whenever his name comes up! And that is: that he was a sickly lad, he couldn't go down below, so he was allowed to stay up and play the organ and write these brilliant songs, and all the institutions that he was too sickly to join in with have gone: mining's gone, the Bank of Cornwall's gone, all those big buildings are used for other things – if they're there at all – and who would have thought that the most esoteric, the flimsiest, the thing that could blow away in the breeze most easily – his music – that's still going!'

Hark the Glad Sound THOMAS MERRITT(1863-1908), words PHILIP DODDRIDGE (1702-1751)

CD 1 Track 12

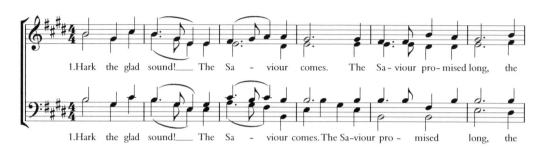

1.Hark the glad sound!___ The Sa - viour comes. The Sa-viour pro-mised long, the

1.Hark the glad sound!___ The Sa - viour comes. The Sa-viour pro - mised long, the

Sa - viour pro - mised___ long! Let ev'-ry heart pre - pare___ a throne,

Sa - viour pro - mised long! Let ev'-ry heart pre - pare a throne,

And ev' - ry voice a song, and

Let ev' - ry heart___ pre - pare a___ throne, And ev' - ry voice a___

And

Let ev' - ry heart___ pre - pare a throne,

ev' - ry voice a song,

song,_____ And ev'_____ ry voice a song.

ev' - ry voice a song,

And ev' - ry voice a___ song, And ev' - ry voice a song.

Hark the Glad Sound
As sung by the Harmony Choir, Falmouth, Christmas Eve 2016

1. Hark, the glad sound! The Saviour comes
The Saviour promised long
Let every heart prepare a throne
And ev'ry voice a song.

2. He comes the prisoners to release
In Satan's bondage held
The gates of brass, before Him burst
The iron fetters yield.

3. (*often sung elsewhere*)
 He comes the broken heart to bind
The bleeding soul to cure
And with the treasures of His grace
To enrich the humble poor.

4. Our glad hosannas, Prince of Peace
Thy welcome shall proclaim
And Heav'n's eternal arches ring
With thy beloved name.

Hark the Glad Sound (Port Isaac)

The eighteenth century was the period when hymn-singing really caught on, thanks to writers associated with the Wesleyan revival, and the words for this carol were written then in 1735 by Philip Doddridge.

He was born in 1702 in London, the youngest of twenty children. He became one of the dissenting clergy at Kibworth, Leicestershire, and later was pastor at the Castle Hill Independent Chapel in Northampton from 1739 until his death. Here he became the 'founder and director of an academy for the training of young nonconformists who were refused, because of their non-conformity, admission to the English Universities' (E. Routley, *Hymns and Human Life*, 1952). He was described as having 'wide sympathies and a gentle, unaffected goodness' (John Julian, *Dictionary of Hymnology*, 1907). He was friends with the well known hymn writer Isaac Watts and welcomed the work of Wesley and Whitefield. He died of tuberculosis in 1751 in Lisbon, Portugal, where he'd gone to recuperate from exhaustion.

His hymns, of which there are many, were published after his death and subsequently enthusiastically taken up by the Methodists. Although 'Hark the Glad Sound' is known as an 'Advent hymn', Dodderidge himself entitled it as 'Christ's Message' and

Port Isaac Chorale in rehearsal in the Old Temperance Hall, Port Isaac, 2015

intended it to be sung all year round. The words closely follow the ministry of Jesus in St Luke in the Bible. It was very popular and can be found in 732 hymnals, the majority of which are associated with the tune 'Richmond'. However there are many other melodies linked to the words, and most famously of course, in Cornwall, is Thomas Merritt's version. We also heard another melody in Bude from the collection of Bert Tape from Morwenstow, with an unknown composer. Another is in a collection called *Christmas Carols*, 1923, also by Dunstan, where he uses Jarman's tune 'Lyngham', better known in Cornwall as a tune to 'While Shepherds Watched'. 'Hark the Glad Sound' appears in both Warmington and Barnicoat's collections where both tunes are the same starting with a 'proclaimed' first line similar to this version which is from Port Isaac but then differ significantly. It could be that these are much older versions than the one by Merritt as the manuscripts for the Barnicoat collection could date from as early as the beginning of the eighteenth century.

As far as we're aware the Port Isaac version is not known elsewhere. As Janet Townsend, the MD of Port Isaac Chorale told us: *'The carol that is truly Port Isaac, is Hark the Glad Sound'*. One of the singers, Joan, added: *'We used to think it was unique to Port Isaac, for a while, but then after, we knew it was. Definite'*.

Our first recording visit away from the Redruth area was to Port Isaac, early in December 2015. We had made the long drive from home to hear the Port Isaac Chorale under the leadership of Janet Townsend, on their rehearsal night in the old Temperance Hall. One of the singers had heard us interviewed about the project on Radio Cornwall and had suggested that we come up to hear their carols. This was a real treat for us and reinforced our feeling that we were doing the right thing, as we heard a number of carols that we didn't know, including this version of 'Hark the Glad Sound'. Unsurprisingly, amongst their regular Christmas repertoire there is a crossover of material with that of nearby Padstow, including 'Angels From the Realms of Glory'

sung to the tune 'Calcutta', and 'Mountains' (otherwise known as 'How Beautiful Upon the Mountains'). But they also have some carols which we believe to be uniquely theirs: a lovely setting of Christina Georgina Rossetti's poem 'Love Came Down at Christmas', sung to the tune 'Tregarthen', which was written by C. E. Hoskin, who had been organist at Roscarrack Chapel in Port Isaac, and 'Hark! Hark'! as remembered by George Steer.

Janet has lived in Port Isaac all her married life, since 1967, and in 1971 she decided to revive the singing in the village. There had been a choir in the thirties, and one of their singers, Jack Collins, was known as the Fisherman Bass, and had broadcast as far back as the twenties. Janet formed the Port Isaac Singers, a ladies choir, which about twenty-five years ago became a mixed choir when some of the men wanted to become involved. They are now known as Port Isaac Chorale. *'One of the first concerts we did as a*

Top: Port Isaac Chorale with Truro Music Festival shield in the 1990s

Below: Old Port Isaac Choir with the same shield in the 1930s

mixed choir was an anniversary concert of when the original Port Isaac Choir were formed in the 1930s. We'd won the same shield that they'd won forty or fifty years before!' (Janet Townsend)

Janet recognised the importance of preserving the local carols and transcribed them from the singing of those who still remembered them. One of these singers, Joan, told us that these songs were learnt by ear: *'We were brought up with singing, our parents, everything, and it was always the thing at Christmas, that all the men, they'd go in pubs and they'd come out from there and go over chapel, they'd have all the carols over there and after chapel they'd come out and they'd all congregate down on the Platt. They'd start singing. "Right, strike sound, Frank!" and he'd strike the note. Frank would always strike the note, he had a lovely tenor voice, Frank Masters. Well, we was allowed to come down then, get out from bed and come down, and this is how we all got involved singing. And the men would be down there on the Platt, and my step-dad, they always used to shove him in the middle of the group, because he was a lovely tenor. My mum had a lovely voice, top soprano. My sister, bless her, was second soprano'.*

Janet told us that: *'Every Christmas in the pub at Port Gaverne, we sing carols, and on Christmas Eve we end up at the Golden Lion here in Port Isaac. When they used to have their candlelit service over at Roscarrick, the men would sit on one side, tenors and basses, ladies on the other side, never the twain should meet. The conductor presumably at the organ; the rest of the congregation downstairs. This is what I reproduced when we started singing over there. It's a continuation of that night'.*

Hark the Glad Sound
As sung by Port Isaac Chorale, in the Port Isaac Temperance Hall, 2015

1. Hark, the glad sound! The Saviour comes
The Saviour promised long
Let every heart prepare a throne
And ev'ry voice a song.

2. He comes the prisoners to release
In Satan's bondage held
The gates of brass, before Him burst
The iron fetters yield.

3. Our glad hosannas, Prince of Peace
Thy welcome shall proclaim
And Heav'n's eternal arches ring
With thy beloved name.

Hark the Glad Sound (Port Isaac) TRADITIONAL words PHILIP DODDRIDGE (1702-1751)

CD 1 Track 13

'There were some of the old miners used to work in the Grenville mine there, they would sing the carols when they would leave work and come up from the shift, and while walking up through. You could hear them. That's the old Christmases see.' (Roy Thomas, ex MD, Troon Toc H Choir, 2016)

Troon's old Toc H choir is now known as Canoryon Trewoon, the current musical director is Andrew Thomas, a man whose links with Troon go back many years and whose father and grandfather sang and whose cousin Roy Thomas was MD before him. Roy told us: *'My grandfather Joseph Thomas, he was organist and choirmaster at the United Methodist Chapel – all the family used to gather at Granny Thomas' Christmas Day, my grandfather would stop the activities and get on the organ and we all had to do a little carol service. Two of his carols he used to sing, one was "Hark What Music", and the other one was "Star of Jacob". They were the first two carols I was taught to play'.*

We know that 'Hark What Music' has an unbroken history of being sung in Troon which makes it feel very special.

'On the morning of Christmas Eve 2015, we went to record Canoryon Trewoon in the square in Camborne. Just brilliant! A lovely group of people, singing wonderfully and so friendly. Many of the carols were ones we'd not heard before, but all were Cornish, and local to this area. The sun came out briefly and it felt like a great start to Christmas Eve!' (Hilary Coleman)

This annual event has continued for many years but sadly their tradition of singing carols through the streets of Troon on Christmas morning stopped only a few years ago. There are several videos of this on YouTube, however, which are well worth looking out for.

Carols by Candlelight, Oswald Pryor cartoon

David Oates a longtime member of Canoryon Trewoon wrote an interesting article for the *Western Morning News* in 2001 in which he describes the Troon tradition:

'Records show that in the 1890s a tradition existed in the village of a group of men – probably drawn, in the main, from the strong Methodist tradition that was found in every mining community – forming an ad hoc choir and singing Cornish carols, unaccompanied, around the streets of the village in the period leading up to Christmas, with the highlight being Christmas Day. These carols were also sung by them, too, as they went below ground to burrow in the darkness of the many local mines – the great Wheal Grenville and the mighty Dolcoath, where the levels would ring with joy at Christmas time. That tradition has continued above ground – with possible breaks in wartime – until the present day, with the great-great-grandsons of

those singers of the 19th century forming the backbone of the choir. For some 50 years now, the singing at Troon has been organised by the local branch of Toc H, an organisation once well known in every Cornish town and village, and which was spawned in the horror of life on the Western Front in the infamous Ypres Salient, providing a sanctuary behind the lines for battle shocked soldiers. After the great conflict the movement transferred its efforts and its principles to the peacetime community, looking after ex-servicemen and civilians alike'.

Canoryon Trewoon in Camborne, Christmas eve, 2015

'Hark, What Music' was clearly popular in Cornwall and its diaspora, with reports of it being sung by the miners in Kimberley, South Africa, in Australia and California, where it remains part of the Grass Valley Cornish Choir's Christmas repertoire. Roy Thomas told us about his two grandfathers going to the Northern states of USA, possibly Michigan: *'My two Grandfathers went to America, they were two opposites – one was on the staff of the mines, my other Grandfather was a miner, underground. He was rough and ready, you know what I mean? He went America with two shilling in his pocket and two cheese sandwiches tied up in a red handkerchief. Camborne Station was packed, from what I've been told, waiting for the train. He started a choir out there, and they were singing this Cornish music, carols'.*

In Cornwall we know that 'Hark What Music' was regularly included in the Christmas repertoire at the Flowerpot Chapel, Redruth, between 1874 and 1904. It was the most popular carol in the records that we viewed, included in fifteen out of eighteen Christmas services. In present-day Cornwall, this carol lives on, sung by the Harmony Choir, Falmouth, Canoryon Trewoon, and the Tregajorran Singers amongst others. Many of these groups sing the Warmington version. However, both the music and lyrics of 'Hark What Music' were first published in Heath's collection in 1889 attributed to Thomas Broad of Illogan. It also appears in many other collections and these later publications all have different arrangements of the same melody. It is worth noting

Troon Toc H Choir, Troon, 1974

how this tune has developed; being a good example of the way a favourite carol evolves with use. Heath's version is comparatively simple, reminiscent of 'Awake Ye Nations', yet Warmington's is a more complicated version with flourishes and fugues.

In Troon there is also a long tradition of an annual Carolaire. Rachel Vaughan, soprano soloist and Troon born and bred, told us her memories of growing up on a farm in the middle of Troon in the 1980s, and about the Carolaire:

'My family were a big Methodist family and music started for me in the chapel. My aunts and uncles, my mum, they all sang in various choirs locally. My earliest memories of singing Merritt's and Nicholas' carols were actually in the family around Christmas. We used to have epic parties at my Gran's that would last from about twelve noon to about midnight. My aunt used to play the piano, and amongst the family we had all four parts. We would all start off on the air, and gradually some of the boys would learn the men's parts, and so we would sing in four parts! Then when I was about ten I went up into the choir for the Carolaire for the first time. Round about that time I was starting to take music quite seriously, instrumentally as well, but it still felt quite daunting to be up in that choir in the Carolaire even though I knew the music!

They call it an augmented choir, people come from all over to sing in it and it is completely unrehearsed. I think a lot of people who sing locally know each other, and they come as individuals, but there will be two or three people from Holman Climax, and two or three people from somewhere else, and they just know the carols, which is a real testament to how well known they are in this area. That's what I've always found really interesting, it just relied upon the fact that people grew up knowing these carols and they were part of our cultural DNA.

We do the same carols every year, about ten Merritt, one Nicholas and one Warmington. Andrew Thomas is the conductor every year, and Colin Parnell, the organist, has played without a break for forty years, and he organises the whole thing as well. Often the choir will outnumber the congregation, but that's all part of it!

I think the carol tradition has the most crossover of anything in music between the chapels and pubs and those carols are sung as hymns and they're sung in the pub and on the street corners and everywhere else. I think that's really important.'

Hark What Music T. BROAD (?-1848)

CD 1 Track 14

Hark What Music
As sung by Canoryon Trewoon at Camborne on Christmas Eve, 2015

1. Hark what music fills creation
Circling through the boundless sky
Shepherds filled with consternation
Hear seraphic harmony.

2. See them from the realms of glory
Shedding lustre o'er the morn
While they chant the wondrous story
Of the great Messiah born.

3. Go to Bethlehem: in a manger
There you'll see the Saviour King
Come and see the heavenly stranger
Make the whole creation ring.

Hellesveor

'The best I've heard Hellesveor sound, strangely enough, was on an August evening as we sung it outside Treloyan Manor. Oh golly! You could hear it ringing down through! That was special! They had some guests up there, and they asked the choir to come up and sing to them. I'm not sure if they were from America, or wherever, but they wanted to hear Cornish Carols. Even in August! We don't usually start practising Christmas carols until after harvest. It's not like we're superstitious or anything, we've usually got so many other things going on.' (William Thomas, St Ives Choirmaster, 2016).

The week before Christmas 2015 saw us heading west to St Ives for their annual carol concert in the Fore Street Chapel. *'Squeezed between a mass of other buildings right on the harbour it was a wonderful location to hear these St Ives carols. A very moving concert: beautiful singing with real feeling, the sermons were quite moving too and the whole evening had a timeless quality to it. Yet we knew so few of these carols, apart from a couple of Merritt's, and realised that St Ives has its own repertoire of carols which predominantly come from the Warmington collection. However the carol we had come down to record was not in this collection yet it was the finale to the evening and the whole congregation, young and old, rose to sing… Hellesveor… perfect!'* (Hilary Coleman)

The evening's singing was conducted by William Thomas, St Ives-born, and MD of the St Ives Community Choir, the St Ives Carol Choir and the Fore Street Chapel Choir. William started each verse by 'lining out', singing the first line on one note in his wonderful, rich voice, they call it 'strike sound' as in Padstow and other places along the north coast. William told us: *At Christmas we sang the Cornish carols around the piano and*

learnt them that way. My uncles and aunties, cousins, we all sang. We used to sing in each other's houses, and that's what we did when we met together – we sang! Out carolling, we used to gather in a ring, in a circle, and we, as youngsters, were put in front, on the inside of the circle so that people could sing in our ears. That's how we learned. Didn't have any words, didn't have any music; it was dark anyway. You had to learn it by rote'.

At one time, each chapel in St Ives had its own choir: United Chapel in Bedford Road, Wesleyan Chapel, Hellesveor, Halsetown, Zion Congregational, Salvation Army, Fore Street Primitive, Bible Christian. The majority of these also had a carol choir, so at Christmas the streets would be filled with the sound of carols.

CHRISTMAS CAROLS

SET TO MUSIC BY THE LATE

COLAN WILLIAMS

ST. IVES.

JACOBS LTD., PRINTERS, ST. IVES.

Above: Hellesveor Chapel

Left: Colan Williams cover, words only, 1920s

St Ives carollers on Christmas Eve 2005 at Mount Zion, St. Ives, overlooking the harbour

They would follow each other around, avoiding being too close so that they didn't clash, listening out for each other. William told us that *'When you stopped singing, you'd go "Oh, 'ark! They're up there, Hellesveor are up there, we'll go this way!" There was no ill feeling, no animosity'.*

Back in William's childhood, collecting boxes were taken round with the singers, collecting money for the upkeep of the chapels. *'They used to walk miles of an evening, and they used to go out the week before and the week after Christmas. Nowadays Christmas seems to finish on Boxing Day, but in those days they'd go on, carolling around the streets of St Ives till Twelfth Night. Even if they weren't involved in chapel themselves, the local people knew that every night there would be carol choirs going out: They would come out to the door and listen: "Oh! That was 'andsome! Can we 'ave another one! Can we 'ave such and such, that's my favourite!" There would be great laughter as well! My father, oh he was a character! He was out one day with the carol choir, and they were singing in a circle and he climbed up this lamp post and made faces at the ladies, and one looked up and saw father and laughed and her teeth fell out in the middle of the ring! I picture now, some of the older people, when we used to go around, a lot of people would be housebound and their faces used to light up! "Come in 'ere my cheeld! Come in 'ere! Have something to drink, do you? Or 'ave a nicey! 'Ere!" Lovely! But, all the houses were occupied, people in all the houses, and they would come out'.* (William Thomas)

Today, for various reasons there is less carolling in the streets: the chapels have diminished in congregation size or closed down, there is just the St Ives Carol Choir

now amalgamated from all the chapel choirs. The local people are spread further apart due to the huge increase in second and holiday homes in the town, so many of the houses in the centre are unoccupied in the wintertime or if they are the occupants come from elsewhere with no knowledge of the tradition. Therefore, the carol concert in Fore Street Chapel fulfils a need, allowing older, less mobile people the opportunity to still hear and sing their old carols, without having to face walking and standing out in the cold. But, don't be fooled into thinking it's only the oldies! When we were there, we saw quite young children in the congregation, singing along, especially with Hellesveor – boding well for the continuation of this tradition.

Tommy Banfield (1910-1990), Halsetown Chapel Choir leader

Katrina Geraghty started the St Ives Community Choir in 2004 and when she gave up the choir in 2011 William Thomas took it over. Katrina, who was the Secondary School Head of Music at St Ives, is related to Tommy Banfield (1910-1990), a well-known local clarinetist, and one time leader of Halsetown Choir who was a great enthusiast, friend and assistant to Colan Williams, the composer of 'Hellesveor'. Katrina remembers her Uncle Tommy doing 'Hellesveor' when she was just a young child. *'You always stand up for Hellesveor in St Ives! "All stand for Hellesveor!" At rehearsals they would often have a euphonium for the bass, a tenor horn for the tenor, a cornet for the alto and a clarinet* (Tommy) *for the soprano. The instruments would give the notes for the people to learn the parts. That was how they picked it up'.* William Thomas also remembers singing with instruments: *'My father was the leader of the Bible Christian Carol Choir and we would borrow a couple of instruments from the Town Band. There'd be a cornet and a euphonium. The cornet would take the soprano part; the euphonium would play either the alto part or the tenor part depending on how many people were there. Some of the other chapels, Fore Street Chapel and Halsetown Chapel had clarinets. Tommy Banfield was up Halsetown'.*

It was Katrina who popularised 'Hellesveor' with the community choir: *'With St Ives Combined Chapels Choir, Edward Perkin held it all together after Tommy Banfield. "Hellesveor" was always taught through the chapels, but I gave non-Chapel goers the chance to learn "Hellesveor". My aim was to get children, grandparents, parents, friends, aunties, uncles, a little lady who perhaps didn't go out and didn't have many friends singing – at one time we had 113 members on our books. In 2005, learning "Hellesveor" with the community choir – Richard Harry Rowe and Edward Charles Paynter, came up to help the men and at the St Ives School Christmas Concert the Community Choir, sang "Hellesveor"'.*

So 'Hellesveor' became very much the St Ives carol although it has now been taken up by other choirs. It is a real challenge to sing and one singer is known to have called it 'Hell's Teeth'! It was composed in 1908 by Colan 'Cully' Williams and was named after the chapel, near St Ives, where Cully, who had been blinded in a mine accident, was the organist. William remembers singing for Cully's sister: *'We always had to go outside his sis-*

ter's house, Wesley Passage, and sing, and she would come out; little, short, dumpy lady.'

There is a small booklet of the words to twenty one carols entitled *Christmas Carols Set to Music by the Late Colan Williams* (no date), which contains 'Hellesveor' as well as See the Morning which is another St Ives favourite. Also Tommy Banfield's manuscripts of 'Hellesveor' and other carols by Cully have been described as works of art in themselves, and are now preserved in the Royal Cornwall Museum.

'The carol choir is different to any other, in that singing outdoors is what we call giving it belltink! There's no contrast, it's just giving it belltink! The sound goes away from you, and you just sing out really! And the breathing is not ideal, because they take a breath where they can! So the phrasing of it is not ideal. Carols just have a feel of their own, it's what makes them different. Blessed to be a part of that, what is now history, really. It is special. I know everybody will say that in their own generation something was special. But just to be a part of the sound of it, it won't be like that again, but I was part of it! It was lovely and we had some beautiful singers, and some great characters'. (William Thomas)

Hellesveor
As sung at the Fore Street Chapel, St Ives, December 2015

Lo, the shepherds were abiding
With their flocks on Bethle'ms plains
When they heard the joyful tidings
Sung in sweet angelic strains

As the sacred chords were ringing,
Lo, an Heavenly voice did cry
Fear not mortals, we are bringing
Peace to earth from Heaven most high

Coda:
Glory to God in the highest
And on earth be peace

Hellesveor COLAN WILLIAMS (1908)

CD 1 Track 15

sung ___ in ___ sweet an - gel - - ic strains,
peace ___ to ___ earth from heav'n most high,

sung in sweet an - gel - - ic ___ strains,
peace to earth ___ from heav'n most ___ high,

sung in sweet an - ge - lic strains,
peace to earth from heav'n most high,

sung ___ in
peace ___ to ___

sung in sweet an - gel - ic strains. When they heard the
peace to earth from heav'n most high. Fear not mor - tals

sweet ___ an - gel - ic strains. ___ When they heard the joy - ful tid - ings
earth ___ from heav'n most high. ___ Fear not mor - tals we are bring-ing

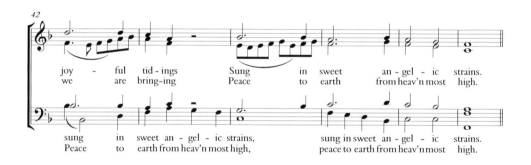

joy - ful tid - ings Sung in sweet an - gel - ic strains.
we are bring-ing Peace to earth from heav'n most high.

sung in sweet an - gel - ic strains, sung in sweet an - gel - ic strains.
Peace to earth from heav'n most high, peace to earth from heav'n most high.

Coda after verse 2

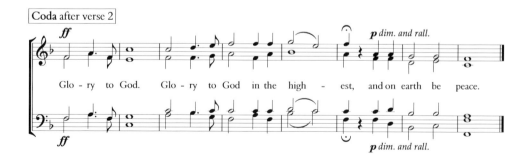

_ff_   _p dim. and rall._

Glo - ry to God. Glo - ry to God in the high - est, and on earth be peace.

_ff_   _p dim. and rall._

Karol, Karol Kristyon (Carol, Carol Christians)

This carol is printed in Dunstan's book as 'Carol, Carol, Christians' and Dunstan says: 'this simple but tuneful carol was formerly very popular in Cornwall. The melody and the words – which vary considerably from other versions – were communicated in 1912, by A. Wellington Esq., organist for several years of Truro Wesleyan Church'.

The melody is by Matthew Burrows, a cooper and parish clerk in Lanivet and was written in 1850. The tune was subsequently arranged by Ralph Dunstan, who doesn't give the author for the words. However, a very different version of the words, with only the first two lines being the same, is by Bishop Arthur C. Coxe (1818–1896), who was the second Bishop of Western New York, and they are printed in *Christian Ballads*, 1840. This version of the carol, with music by R. F. Smith, features in *Carols for Use in Church* by Richard R. Chope, 1875, with the interesting comment: 'in the early ages Bishops were accustomed to sing carols among the clergy. Bishop Aldhelm sang sacred songs to his harp on bridges and in thoroughfares'. The carol as collected by Dunstan has a more ballad-like narrative and therefore could well be an earlier version.

As far as we know there are no surviving carols written in the Cornish language although we have a tantalising reference to the language and carols in the following passage from *Antiquities Cornuontanic*, Scawen's *Dissertation on the Cornish Tongue*, written about 1683. Scawen describes the old 'Guirremears' (literally Great Plays, alluding to the Miracle Plays performed in the Plen an Gwariow around Cornwall) as a 'great

Carol singers at Hoopers Bridge, Lanivet, 1940

Keur Heb Hanow at Bridge Chapel, 2015

means to keep in use the tongue with delight and admiration, and it continued also friendship and good correspondency in the people', and goes on to add, 'They also had their carols at several times, especially at Christmas, which they solemnly sung, and sometimes used, as I have heard, in their churches after prayers, the burden of which songs 'Nowell, Nowell, good news, good news of the Gospel' by which means they kept the use of the tongue the better'. He gives this as an example of how carols helped keep the language alive, however R. Morton Nance, in the *Old Cornwall* journal of 1957, thinks that 'Scawen imagined that Nowell was Cornish (a)n Awayl – the Gospel – and that like Gospel it meant Good News and from this went on to assume that carols in which Nowell was sung must have originally been in Cornish, with a burden, "an Awayl, newodhow da a'n Awayl". It is difficult to account in any other way for his statement'.

In spite of this lack of original Cornish language carols the group Keur Heb Hanow (Choir with No Name), are promoting the Cornish language through their translations of carols known in Cornwall. We recorded them at the annual concert of Cornish carols at Bridge Chapel, near Illogan. They are a mixed voice group of six singers with flute and piano accompaniment and three members of the choir are bards of the Cornish Gorsedd. As they say: *'We have strong links to the Heamoor Cornish Language Class and we first came together in 2012 to enter the Traditional Cornish Carol Class at the Cornwall Music Festival in Truro, singing in Cornish only, which we have continued to do since then'.*

They are regularly invited to perform at various Cornish language meetings and events and have recorded a CD called *Karolyow Nadelik* (2015). The choir says 'we hope that people will enjoy listening to the carols both for the music and for the pleasure of exploring the Cornish language and so to that end, we have included the words on the insert both in Cornish and English'.

'Karol, Karol, Kristyon' was translated into Cornish by John Parker who is a teacher at the Heamoor Cornish class. The choir also has a personal link to this carol: 'like many people in Cornwall we love singing the uplifting pieces written by Thomas Merritt but there is another, more unusual, carol that has become the group's favourite. Our flautist, Mary Jones, has fond memories of hearing 'Carol, Carol, Christians' sung in her native Lanivet when she was growing up, and her enthusiasm for it has rubbed off on the rest of us. It is unusually gentle.' (*Western Morning News,* 2015)

While researching this carol a number of emails were sent between us and Stephen Penhaligon of Keur Heb Hanow. In one, he replied that they sang the Duncan version. We were a little surprised – we hadn't come across this particular arranger before, so we asked Stephen about him. This was his reply: *'I meant Dunstan. Duncan is the man who mends our boiler and he just happened to be here at the time I was writing the e-mail. His setting of the carol is of no great interest.'*

Carol, Carol Christians
(English words as in Dunstan)

Carol, carol Christians, carol joyfully
Carol for the coming of Christ's Nativity
In the fields abiding, watching through the night
Bethlehem's simple shepherds saw a glorious sight.

Chorus:
Carol, carol Christians, carol joyfully
Carol for the coming of Christ's Nativity, carol, carol.

All was still and silent, When o'er hills around
Stream'd a glorious radiance, with sweet harmonious sound
Came a holy Angel, all in light array'd
Glory shone upon them – and they were sore afraid.

"Fear not," said the Angel, "Tidings glad I bring
For in lowly manger, this night is born a king
Now in David's city, born is Christ the Lord
Born to be the Saviour, By heav'n and earth ador'd.

Suddenly appearing, came an Angel throng
Praising God and singing a glorious Heav'nly song
"In the Highest Glory! On the earth be peace!
Peace, goodwill from Heaven begin and never cease.

Carol, carol Christians! Carol joyfully
Carol for the coming of Christ's Nativity
Now a gladsome Christmas to all Christian men!
Carol, carol gladly, for Christmas comes again.

Karol, Karol Kristyon MATTHEW BURROWS (1850), Cornish translation

John Parker. *As sung by Keur Heb Hanow at Bridge Chapel concert, 2015*
CD 1 Track 16

1. Ka - rol, Ka - rol Kris - tyon, Kan u - ghel dha lev,
2. Pup - tra oll o ko - sel pan dheuth gor - mo - la deg,
3. Dhe - dha 'medh an el, 'Na ber - thewgh hwi own mann,
4. Dis - towgh y teuth routh veur a e - ledh, lu an nev, Ow
5. Ka - rol, ka - rol Kris - tyon, Kan u - ghel dha lev,

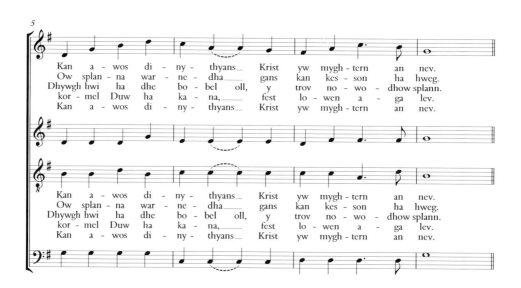

Kan a - wos di - ny - thyans Krist yw mygh - tern an nev.
Ow splan - na war - ne - dha gans kan kes - son ha hweg.
Dhywgh hwi ha dhe bo - bel oll, y trov no - wo - dhow splann.
kor - mel Duw ha ka - na, fest lo - wen a - ga lev.
Kan a - wos di - ny - thyans Krist yw mygh - tern an nev.

Unison

Dres an nos ow kwi - tha a - ga flock y'n pras,
Gwis - kys oll yn go - low, kan - nas Duw an Tas,
Rag yn pre - sep u - vel yw ge - nys Sel - wyas klor,
Gor - dhyans yn u - ghel - der re bo dhe Dhuw a ras,
Peub oll gwres ka - na rag lem - myn, ott, dhyn ni Re

Bu - ge - ledh a Veth - lem, a vi - ras mar - thus bras.
El a om - dhi - skwe - dhas, own a's te - a bras.
Krist an ar - lodh gor - dhys yn fen yn nev ha'n nor.
Kres y'n bys dhe vab - den ha' y vo - lon - jedh mas.
dheuth Na - de - lik lo - wen ar - ta, yn pur dhe - vri.

Chorus

Ka - rol, ka - rol, Kris - tyon, Kan u - ghel dha lev, Kan a - wos di -
Ka - rol, ka - rol, Kris - tyon, Kan u - ghel dha lev, Kan a - wos di -
Ka - rol, ka - rol, Kris - tyon, Kan u - ghel dha lev, Kan a - wos di -
Ka - rol, ka - rol, Kris - tyon, Kan u - ghel dha lev, Kan a - wos di -

-ny - thyans Kris yw mygh - tern an nev. Ka - rol, Ka - rol.
-ny - thyans Kris yw mygh - tern an nev. Ka - rol, Ka - rol.
-ny - thyans Kris yw mygh - tern an nev. Ka - rol, Ka - rol.
-ny - thyans Kris yw mygh - tern an nev. Ka - rol, Ka - rol.

Rouse, Rouse

'I desire to bring to your notice an original Cornish Carol, the words and music of which have been handed down by oral tradition and have never been printed … the family tradition is that it is two hundred years old, but one expert places it at about 1780, while another thinks it is as late as 1800 or 1820.' (Lady Molesworth St Aubyn, Old Cornwall Society talk, Newquay, 1922)

We drove up to Padstow one dark evening in December 2015 to meet the carollers and walk with them around the streets as they sang their local carols to the town's residents. The singers were really friendly and we were able to chat as we went from house to house. They sang in the streets and called on elderly people who joined in from their doorways and were obviously delighted to see the carollers. That is part of the tradition, the visits to people who love the carols, old Padstownians, particularly those who had been a part of the carolling fraternity. One of the carollers later told us: *'I would add though that these places are getting fewer and fewer. There are far less people now to sing to than there used to be. The emphasis has changed a little bit insomuch as the routes are slightly less than they used to be, and the older characters aren't with us anymore. There's less people to sing to. Also the old Padstownians are more scattered around the area of Padstow, not concentrated in the town centre any longer.'*

We saw a real mix of men, women and children come together to sing carols, with the boys standing amongst the tenors and the girls with the sopranos, picking up the parts as their parents and grandparents before them must have done. A friend, Jenny Crowe, was there, and she was obviously a mainstay for the women singers, and the young girls shared funny moments with her pretending to sing the bass parts!

The carols sung that night were from Padstow's own carolling tradition: some we knew from other parts of Cornwall, but two, 'Rouse, Rouse' and 'Jesse', we were not aware of being sung anywhere else. Two of the carollers, Roger Gool and John Buckingham, later gave us an insight as to how carols travelled from one part of Cornwall to another: *"Harky, Harky" is believed to have come up with the Porthleven fishermen when they used to put into port, pre-war, and would join the carollers and sing their carols. Also Mount's Bay fishermen came up at Christmas time. We've never picked up any carols from the east coast, although they were in port from February to May, in large numbers. But of course they weren't here at Christmas! They may have their own carol tradition but they're not going to sing them at Easter!'*

During our research we visited the Cornwall Records Office in Truro, where we saw a small notebook for the Register of Services, from St Petroc's Church, Little Petherick, three miles from Padstow. This book dates from October 1858 to 1861, and contains notes written by the Rector, the Reverend Sir Hugh Henry Molesworth (1818-1862). Amongst these notes he mentions carols and hymns that were sung at various services, and 'Rouse, Rouse' is included in Christmas services in 1858, 1859 and 1861. There is also a mention of instruments played, bass viol and flutes, along with 'Bass and treble singers from St Issey and St Merryn'. The rector's descendent, the Reverend Sir St Aubyn Hender Molesworth St Aubyn was married to Ingeborg Lady

Molesworth St Aubyn, who talked of 'family tradition' in the quote at the head of this section, and who read a paper about 'Rouse, Rouse' at a meeting of the Newquay Old Cornwall Society in October 1922, where the carol was also sung. The *Journal of the Royal Institution of Cornwall*, 1923, which reported this, also tells us of Mrs Ellen Lobb who was 87 at the time, and who had lived all her life in Penrose, St Ervan, near Padstow. When she was a child Mrs Lobb was taught 'Rouse Rouse' by her grandfather, Mr Tippet, also of Penrose. Mrs Lobb's niece, Miss Old, of Helland School, and her son, William Lobb, who was bandmaster of Wadebridge Town Band, took down the words and music respectively, from her singing. This version was printed by the Novello Company in 1922 – and cost 2d! It was also printed in the *Old Cornwall Journal* of 1923. Lady Molesworth thought that the lines, 'And straight away the shepherds, To Bethlehem steered' suggested a sea-coast origin, tying in nicely with the premise that this carol was written in Padstow. She also said: 'I had the pleasure of hearing Mrs Lobb sing her carol with a volume of voice surprising to one so feeble. She must have once been a fine singer.' The Molesworth-St Aubyns still live at Pencarrow, which is where we went to record 'Calm on the Listening Ear of Night'.

A similar version was sent to Baring-Gould for his collection around 1905 by Mr J. W. Yeale from St Issey, not far from Padstow, who said he had heard it sung when he was a boy thirty years earlier in the 1870s.

This carol also features in Dunstan's *Cornish Song Book*, and he says he has 'reprinted,

Padstow carollers, 2010

by permission, and with some slight simplification of the Harmony' from the *Journal of the Royal Institution of Cornwall*. He has however changed the coda as sung in Padstow because he doubted if it belonged to this carol, and that it 'had undergone much corruption', saying: 'I have replaced it by a reliable version from old MSS in my possession. My own MS copy which must have been transcribed over 60 years ago [1860s] has (in addition to the vocal parts) the instrumental parts for bassoon and flute here given'.

As you can see this carol has a solid tradition in this area, although we cannot say who wrote it or when. When we returned on our fact-finding visit, we met some of the singers in Padstow Museum, and were able to ask them what they thought of 'Rouse, Rouse' and we loved their answers:

'When I was very young and first started singing the carols I couldn't ever remember them starting with anything else. "Rouse, Rouse" was always the first carol. That would be my favourite too. Instinctively, you know, it's special' (Roger Gool).

'I think that sums up the Padstow carols, that's the main one: "Rouse, Rouse". The most important one.' (Barbara Bassett).

'It has a beat, almost like the Mayday drum' (John Buckingham).

During our visit to the museum, John showed us a programme from 1950 and said: *'Christmas Eve, Christmas Day, New Year's Eve, community carols around the Christmas tree in Broad Street. Started off with a community carol … guess what? "Rouse, Rouse", led by Padstow Town Band'*. It is interesting to note that they called these carols community carols, showing that they must have been well known and been very familiar to the people of Padstow in the 1940s.

The Padstow carollers are not a choir as such, as they do not practise, but just come together for a few occasions before Christmas. They sing mainly outdoors and unaccompanied, the only instrumental music heard is the pitch-pipe before the start of each carol!

'Handed down from generation to generation by word of mouth, learning the individual parts was primarily based on listening to others. More recently, word-sheets and a booklet containing both words and music have appeared in print. The season may begin with perhaps thirty to forty singers, but as the weeks progress, that figure can easily exceed eighty. In the past, over a hundred singers on a Christmas Eve was by no means unusual.' (Roger Gool, *The Padstow Carollers* article)

'When I first started singing them (mid 1950s) it was a very small group of people who went out and they were nearly all from the Methodist Chapel … when I was home I would go out quite regularly and learnt the carols by going out with them, and listening to people who sang the alto part.' (Barbara Bassett)

In the 1960s there was a general resurgence of interest in folk music, which was particularly strong in Cornwall, and in Padstow there were a number of people, Stephen Fuller, Johnny Worden and a few others, who were really anxious that their carolling tradition should not die out. Stephen came from a Methodist background, and was made a bard of the Cornish Gorsedd in 1962, taking the bardic name *Map Pyscajor*, meaning 'Fisherman's Son'. He was the driving force behind a campaign to get younger people to join in the carolling, printing words so that everybody could join in. This led

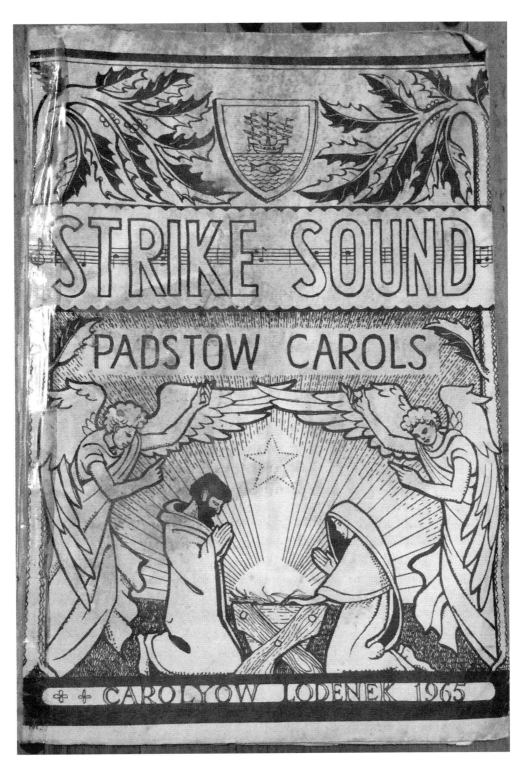

to the publication of *Strike Sound*, a booklet of Padstow Carols, first published in 1971. Inglis Gundry helped with the production of the book, writing a foreword as well as transcribing the music. The rather lovely woodcuts accompanying the book were done by a local lady, Mary Martin.

Edgar Tonkin, Padstow Bandmaster and caroller in the mid 1900s had written down the carols, perhaps the first time for many of them, and these manuscripts somehow ended up in a chest in the church. In the late fifties or early sixties the Reverend Clarke found the manuscripts and passed them to Edgar's son, who in turn passed them on to Stephen Fuller, and they became part of the basis on which *Strike Sound* was written. An interesting title, it comes from the first words of the carol sung at the appropriate pitch, at the start, giving the sopranos their note. The altos, tenors and basses, through years of experience, get their note from there, some perhaps coming in a bar or two into the carol as they find their pitch. We discovered this term used elsewhere along the north coast and it most likely comes from the striking of a tuning fork to give a note. There is a description of this in a letter to the *Western Morning News* from W. D. Wood-Rees in 1924 who talked about the carol-singing tradition in Poundstock: *'I often look back with pleasure at the quaint old Cornish customs of going round Christmas singing on Christmas Eve. The musical instruments were a bass viol, fiddles, flutes and sometimes a clarionet* [sic]. *On the arrival of the choir you would hear them "strick* [sic] *sound" to see if their instruments and voices were in accord'.*

While we were recording carols in nearby Port Isaac, we had been given 'one of Stephen's duplications', an incomplete but early, duplicated, handwritten version of *Strike Sound*, before it was published.

After the publication of *Strike Sound* there was a noticeable increase of interest in singing the Padstow carols, and it was realised that some had slipped out of use. Mike O'Connor, who lives nearby, has been instrumental in getting some of these back in to the Padstow repertoire.

Roger Gool, the current leader of the Padstow carollers, told us that Frank Bray had been the leader of the carollers in the post-war years, *'Frank was followed by Johnny Worden. Mollie Pinch took over from Johnny in about 1972, then Uncle Raymond, but Uncle Raymond died in 1981. Mollie then took it on again and led the Carollers from 1981 until her death in 2005 at the age of ninety-three. I took over leadership from Mollie who approached me around about 2000 to ask me if I would take over from her eventually, so I said, "yeah I'll follow you and you show me what you want me to do!" Unfortunately, the following year, Mollie had a stroke and was unable to speak, and she was like that until she died in 2005. So I didn't really take over until then, that was my first year in charge, and I've been running it ever since.'*

In Roger's article about the Padstow Carollers he describes Mollie as 'the figurehead for the carollers, she always turned up, rain or shine, regardless of the fact that her speech was seriously impaired, she was always there. Popular and with a razor-sharp memory, Mollie's diminutive appearance belied a fierce determination. Her commitment to safeguarding the Padstow carols can never be underestimated.'

Rouse, Rouse
As sung at Padstow, December 2015

Rouse, rouse from your slumbers, prepare a glad voice
And join with the number that now do rejoice
No longer be silent, but now join with them
Archangels are bringing, Archangels are bringing, glad tidings to men!

What blissful glad tidings are those we do hear?
Harmonious rejoicings which sound from the sphere
'Tis music transported, cherubic, profound
Creation's vast circuit it ushers around.

Hark. hark to the chorus, salvation's the theme
To certain poor shepherds appeared on the plain
'Tis Jesus the Saviour, come see where He's born
In Bethlehem's city on this happy morn.

Then straightway those shepherds to Bethlehem steered
Stupendously led by a star that appeared
There Joseph and Mary they saw with surprise
There laid in a Manger, the King of the skies.

Coda:
Angels trump, their message bring, welcome to the new born King!
Mortals join the hosts above, join to sing redeeming love
Hallelujah! Hallelujah! Hallelujah! Let us sing
Hallelujah, praise the Lord! Hallelujah to our new born King!

Rouse, Rouse TRADITIONAL

CD 2 Track 1

Rouse, rouse from your slum - bers, pre - pare a glad voice, And
What bliss - ful glad ti - dings are those we do hear? Har -
Hark, hark to the cho - rus, sal - va - tion's the theme. To
Then straight-way those shep - herds to Beth - le - hem steered, Stu -

join with the num - ber that now do re - joice. No long - er be
mon - ious re - joic - ings which sound from the sphere. 'Tis mu - sic trans -
cer - tain poor shep-herds ap - peared on the plain, 'Tis Je - sus the
pend - ous - ly led by a star that ap - peared. There Jo - seph and

si - lent, but now join with them,
port - ed, che - ru - bic, pro - found;
Sa - viour, come see where he's born:
Ma - ry they saw with sur - prise;

Arch - an - gels are
Cre - a - tion's vast
In Beth - le - hem's
There laid in a

Repeat for other verses

Arch - an - gels are bring - ing glad ti - dings to men.
Cre - a - tion's vast cir - cuit it ush - ers a - round.
In Beth - le - hem's ci - ty on this hap - py morn.
There laid in a man - ger the King of the skies.

bring - ing,
cir - cuit,
ci - ty,
man - ger,

Sapphire Throne

The music to this lovely carol was composed in 1957 by Donald F. Broad who was the organist and choirmaster at the United Methodist Free Church (UMFC), Fore Street, Redruth, also known as the Flowerpot Chapel, and later at the Primitive Methodist Chapel at Plain-an-Gwarry, Redruth. He also gave piano and singing lessons, and composed hymn tunes dedicated to many people and places, including the hymn tune 'Ivy' which he dedicated to his wife, who was a well known soprano soloist.

Clarence and Christabel Maynard outside Flowerpot Chapel. Clarence was lyricist of the 'Sapphire Throne'

We have not been able to confirm a family link to Thomas and Humphrey Broad, but wonder if indeed Donald was carrying on a family tradition and if not was certainly carrying on the strong tradition of carol composing in that area.

The words, written by Clarence Aldrovand Maynard, are dedicated to Aldrovand Maynard, Clarence's father. Aldrovand, who was one of ten children of Richard Maynard, an engineer, of Tuckingmill, seems to have gone out to South Africa as a mining engineer shortly after the death of his father in 1900, where he went on to win fame as a tenor soloist. He came back to Cornwall a few years later, where he became 'one of the most sought after and appreciated tenors in his native Cornwall'. He was known variously as 'The South African tenor', 'The Cornish African tenor', and 'The Camborne and Transvaal tenor'. He was an inventor and made recordings of his singing in 1938. He lived in Tuckingmill, then St Agnes, and later Illogan Highway, and is mentioned in many local newspaper articles between 1907 and 1930 for his wonderful singing performances. He spent time in America in 1923, and died in March 1938. He was described as being 'a likeable personality'. Amongst the many songs he is reported to have sung is 'Star of Bethlehem'. In 1922 he sang in St Day, and Sally likes to think that her grandfather may have heard him sing!

In 1912, he married Myrtle Phillips, also of Tuckingmill and their son, Clarence Aldrovand Maynard, became an electrical engineer and Methodist local preacher, living in Redruth.

We heard this carol at the Bridge Chapel Carol Concert in 2015, sung by Tereba Nessa, Cornish for Until Next Time. They are a choir based at Bridge Chapel, near Illogan, under the leadership of musical director Raymond Basher. They first formed as a temporary choir in January 2012, to sing in the new class for Cornish Christmas Carols at the Cornwall Music Festival in March of that year. They enjoyed singing so much that they decided to stay together to continue singing local Cornish carols, hymns and psalms, and are keen to reverse the decline of local Cornish Christmas carols. They are the official church choir of the Cornish Gorsedd and regularly lead the singing at Cornish language church services. They are proud to say that currently six of their singers have a good knowledge of the Cornish language.

Tereba Nessa had chosen to learn this carol after finding the manuscript in the piano stool in Bridge Chapel! It would seem that the manuscript was published by Dyllansow Truran, a company set up by Len Truran to promote Cornish culture and politics. He

Above: Flowerpot Chapel, Redruth. Built in 1865, destroyed by fire in 1973

Below: Tereba Nessa at Bridge Chapel, 2015

Bridge Chapel, 2017. Due to close in 2018

was a highly influential figure within these fields and became a member of the Cornish political party Mebyon Kernow in 1964. In 1996 the Holyer An Gof award (Truran's bardic name which means 'Follower of Angove') was created in honour of his work and aims to raise the profile of Cornish publishing and writing. After his death some of the manuscripts and original blocks were then acquired by Daryl Curnow who republished some of the carols under the name the Cornish Music Company. This included the carols of Stephen Nicholas and the twelve carols by Thomas Merritt. We also heard 'Sapphire Throne' sung by Canoryon Trewoon.

Fiona Sewell, a friend of Sally's, remembers singing this carol in the Camborne area in the 1950/60s and commented on how much she loved it.

In its mining heyday, Redruth was a thriving town and boasted many Methodist chapels. The United Methodist Free Church built in the early 1800s in Fore Street (now Jim's Cash and Carry), was replaced in the latter part of the century funded mainly by the Trounson brothers who had moved to Redruth from Cury. The new UMFC chapel built across the road from its predecessor became known as Flowerpot Chapel because of the large urns or 'flowerpots' decorating its impressive front. It was a truly impressive building seating almost two thousand people, and was known as Cornwall's Methodist Cathedral. Unfortunately it burnt down in the early 1970s, but is remembered in the name of the car park that now stands on the site.

In the Cornwall Record Office there is a series of Christmas service leaflets from the Flowerpot Chapel dated 1874-1904. This gave us a good insight into what carols were popular then.

The BBC broadcast a Remembrance Service from the Flowerpot Chapel in 1947 and the organist was Donald F. Broad. A leaflet from this occasion says: 'it was looked upon as one of the cathedrals of Cornish Methodism … The church has always been enterprising and has taken a leading part in the cultural life of the town'. Following the broadcast a listener in Liskeard said: *'Their voices came over the air in the good old Cornish style, which added to the reputation of singers from West Cornwall.'*

Sapphire Throne
As sung by Tereba Nessa at the Bridge Chapel Carol Concert, December 2015

In thy wondrous incarnation
Thus we see God's love unveiled
By thy gracious condescension
God to man is now revealed
Stable bare becomes a temple
Cattle stall a sapphire throne
Son of Mary, King of Glory
Deigns to grace a humble home.

Angel hosts declare Thy coming
To the Shepherds with their flocks
Eastern Star now westward roaming
Sheds its beams o'er hills and rocks
Wise men seeking now the reason
For this strange celestial glare
Travel far across the mountains
To present their gifts so rare.

We who worship now the Christ Child
Wing our minds to Bethlehem's Inn
And across the Panorama
Stream the myriads loving Him
Shall we bring a gift less worthy
Than the sages freely gave
Let us now present our praises
To the Lord, who came to save.

Sapphire Throne DONALD F. BROAD, words C. A. MAYNARD

Dedicated to (the late) Aldrovand Maynard. 1957.

CD 2 Track 2

In thy won-drous in - car - na - tion Thus we see God's love un - veiled,
An - gel hosts de - clare thy com - ing To the shep-herds with their flocks.
We who wor - ship now the Christ Child Wing our minds to Beth-l'em's inn.

By thy gra - cious con - de - scen - sion God to man is__ now re - vealed.
Eas - tern Star now east - ward roam - ing Sheds its beams o'er hills and rocks.
And ac - ross the pa - no - ra - ma Stream the my - riads lov - ing him.

Sta - ble bare be - comes a__ tem - ple, Cat - tle stall__ a__ sap-phire throne.
Wise men seek - ing__ now__ the rea - son For this strange ce - les - tial glare,
Shall we__ bring a__ gift__ less wor - thy Than the sa - ges__ free - ly gave.

Son of__ Ma - ry, King of__ glo ry, Deigns to__ grace a__ hum - ble home.
Tra - vel far ac - ross the moun-tains To pre - sent their gifts so rare.
Let us__ now pre - sent our prai - ses To the Lord, who came to save.

'The melodies and words of the carols sung, speak of times far removed from our modern days and to hear "Sound, Sound Your Instruments of Joy" carried on the cold night air forges a link with those who sang the same words in centuries past.' (D. Oates, *Western Morning News* 2001)

This carol, written by W. B. Ninnis, remains very popular in Cornwall and is found in most of the collections made of Cornish carols. The most commonly sung version is in Warmington's publication and that is what we recorded sung by the Cadgwith Singers, on a very wet dark evening in the Halzephron Inn on the Lizard, where they sing carols every year. Appropriately enough Halzephron comes from the Cornish meaning Hell's Cliff. The inn was built in 1468 and many local wrecks have provided the timbers for the building. The Cadgwith Singers have a long reputation in Cornwall for their 'unique, full blooded style of singing that never fails to please' (Paul Collins, *Return to Cadgwith* CD sleeve notes, 2008).

We have known them for many years and they feature in our previous book *Shout Kernow*. David Muirhead, their pitcher-upper, says *'you must always remember we are not a choir, we're just a group of friends who get together to sing the songs we love to sing'*. Their beginnings came from a fisherman's choir that was started by a local preacher in Cadgwith in the early 1900s *'in an attempt to boost his church attendance. The plan failed but he did manage*

Halzephron Inn pub sign, 2015

to consolidate a tradition of singing with a repertoire that has prevailed to the present day'. (Paul Collins)

Paul Collins was there on the evening we visited and not only did we record many of the Cornish carols known elsewhere but we were lucky to record a St Keverne version of 'While Shepherds Watched'. Then Paul and his wife sang a duet of 'What Heavenly Music', a less well known carol by Stephen Nicholas.

The earliest version of the words to 'Seraphic Minstrels' appear on the Woolcock broadsides from Helston in the mid-1800s and then again on those of Harris who was from Hayle. So perhaps it is not too surprising that William Ninnis knew these carol words as he too came from Helston.

The music was first printed in Heath's collection with a simpler fugue and slight variation of words. There is also another in his book written by Thomas Broad and this is very similar to the version they sing in Padstow and is entitled 'Sound, Sound Your Instruments'. The carol has also found its way to Australia where J. H. Thomas did an arrangement of it.

The editors of the *New Book of Oxford Carols* included it, describing it as a Gallery Carol and took it from Barnicoat's collection *Old Cornish Carols*, which is very similar to that in Warmington's.

There have been many recordings of male voice choirs singing the carol and brass arrangements too; the earliest we know of is in 1936 by the Mabe Choir. The *Western Morning News* mentions a recording in 1936 for the programme Sing We Merrily, when the *'BBC Mobile Recording Van travelled recently through Somerset, Dorset and Cornwall in search of carols ... Cornish Carols sung by the Mabe Male Voice Choir, introduced by the choirmaster, the Rev Daly Atkinson'.*

It was from this archive that The Watersons recorded a version of it in 1977. The folklorist A. L. Lloyd said on their sleeve notes:

Porthleven Shoemaker's Shop Choir, 1950s

'Another splendid piece that has dropped out of our hymn books. This anthem, presumably of eighteenth century composition, survived among a few country choirs, chiefly in Devon and Cornwall. The Watersons learnt their version from an old BBC recording of the Mabe Male Voice Choir, from the Penryn district of Cornwall.

The vicar of Mabe reported: "The choir sings as their ancestors did. Such music as they have is in manuscript. They stand in a circle, the leader gives out the first line, and off they go, full tilt. They more or less make up their own harmonies'".

This description certainly fits how it is sung today in the pubs and is how the Cadgwith Singers sang it. A. L. Lloyd links this kind of singing and these old hymns to the American publications of *Southern Harmony* of 1835 and the *Sacred Harp* of 1844, which is also called Shape Note singing because 'it was printed in a kind of patent music notation for the sake of quick learning, still much in use in the upland South'.

Little is known of the composer, William B. Ninnis, but John Speller, an American researcher of Cornish carols has his birth as 1793 and death around 1865. This William ran a bookseller's and shoemaker's business in Meneage Street in Helston. However he married a Jane Bennett and they had a son called William Bennett born in Helston in 1832, who lived there all his life. We think this is more likely to be the correct one. According to the census of 1861 he was a master shoe-maker (like his father) and in 1901 at the age of 68 he was the town postman and a Methodist preacher.

Above: Paul Collins and wife, at Halzephron Inn from the Cadgwith Singers, 2015

In 2004, the *West Briton* ran an article by Martin Matthews entitled 'Bygone Days' with a photo of an 'old men's choir' from the 1950s, who sang around the Lizard area and were also known as the 'Shoemaker's Shop Choir', and who mostly sang carols in the Porthleven square. Perhaps shoemaker shops were similar gathering places to bar-ber shops where men would congregate to sing. There is a lovely reference in an article in the *Cornishman* from 1931, titled 'Christmas in Newlyn Fifty Years Ago', which says: 'there are some of the old boys in Newlyn yet who can look back to the time when we sang our carols in the shoemaker's shop in the Coombe. How delighted our old friend the shoemaker was to hear us sing. I believe his favourite was "Hark, hark, what news the angels bring"'.

Charles Lee, who wrote some wonderful accounts of Cornish life, publishing five novels in the late 19th and early 20th centuries, describes a scene where the men would gather in the shoemaker's shop to talk.

We wonder if the Porthleven choir could even have been the descendant of one that may have gathered at William Ninnis's shop?

Seraphic Minstrels (Sound, Sound) W. B. NINNIS (b. 1832)
CD 2 Track 3

Sound, sound your in - stru-ments of joy, sound, sound your

joy,_____

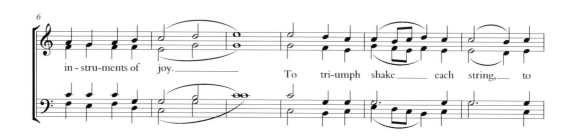

in - stru-ments of joy._____ To tri-umph shake_____ each string,_____ to

tri-umph shake each string.

Let shouts of u - ni - ver - sal joy,_____ of

Let shouts of u - ni - ver-sal joy,_____ of

Let shouts of u - ni - ver-sal joy,_____ of

u - ni - ver-sal joy. Wel - come, wel - come, wel - come a new - born King.

Seraphic Minstrels (Sound, Sound)
As sung by the Cadgwith Singers at Halzephron Inn, December 2015

1. Sound, sound, your instruments of joy
To triumph, shake each string
Let shouts of universal joy,
Welcome your new-born King.

2. See! See the glad'ning dawn appears
Bright angels deck the morn!
Behold, the great I AM is given,
The King of Glory's born!

Also sung elsewhere:
3. Recall the scene, reveal the love
The Lord of Life descend
He left His glorious realms above,
To be the sinners friend!

4. Let heaven and earth and sea proclaim
The wondrous love abroad
And all the universal frame,
Sing praises to our God!

Star of Bethlehem (Lo the Eastern)

A carol hymn known all over Cornwall – one of the top three on our travels. We heard it from Polperro and Padstow to the Lizard and St Just. The music is actually by Samuel Stanley of Birmingham, and dates from 1802-1805 and the lyrics are by Jehoiada Brewer and were written while he was a Congregational minister in Sheffield between 1783 and 1798. It is clearly well known in the North East of England, and in Derbyshire it is one of Coal Aston Carollers' favourite carols, although they sing a variation of the words.

Even so, this carol hymn has strong roots in Cornwall. The earliest reference of the words in Cornwall is on a broadsheet printed by Woolcock of Helston, in the mid 1800s.

The words and music first appear in Heath's *Cornish Carols*, and was also being sung in the Redruth UMFC (Flowerpot Chapel) in 1894, and was in their Christmas service for three years running. Heath attributes it to W. B. Williams (we think this may be a misprint as there was a J. H. Williams who was the organist at the Wesley Chapel in 1889) who could well be the arranger of the Cornish version. Subsequently it was published in nearly all the Cornish carol collections with very similar arrangements. The

JERUSALEM breaks forth in songs,
And deserts learn the joy;
How beautious are their feet,
Who stand on Zion's hill.
Who bring salvation on their tongues,
And words of peace reveal.

How charming is their voice,
How sweet their tidings are;
Zion behold thy Saviour King,
He reigns and triumphs here!
Chorus :— How charming is their voice.

How happy are our ears,
That hear this joyful sound,
Which kings and prophets waited for,
And sought but never found;
How blessed are our eyes,
That see this heavenly light;
Prophets and kings desir'd it long,
But died without the sight!
Chorus :—How charming is their voice.

The watchmen join their voice,
And tuneful notes employ;
The Lord makes bare his arm,
Thro' all the earth abroad;
Let every nation now behold
Their Saviour and their God.
Chorus :—How charming is their voice.

ANGELS from the realms of glory,
Wing your flight o'er all the earth;
Ye who sang creation's story,
Now proclaim Messiah's birth.
Come and worship;
Worship Christ the new-born King.

Shepherds in the field abiding,
Watching o'er their flocks by night;
God with man is now residing,
Yonder shines the infant light.
Come and worship; &c.

Sages leave your contemplations,
Brighter visions beam afar,
Seek the great desire of nations,
Ye have seen his natal star.
Come and worship; &c.

Saints before the altar bending,
Waiting long with hope and fear;
Suddenly the Lord descending,
In his temple shall appear.
Come and worship; &c.

Sinners, wrung with keen repentance,
Doom'd for guilt to endless pain;
Justice now repeals the sentence,
Mercy calls you—break your chains.
Come and worship; &c.

LO! the eastern sages rise,
At a signal in the skies,
Brighter than the brightest gem,
'Tis the star of Bethlehem.

Balaam's mystic words appear,
Full of light divinely clear,
And the import wrapped in them,
Is the star of Bethlehem.

Rocks and deserts can't impede,
On they press no aid they need,
Day and night a guide to them,
Is the star of Bethlehem.

Now the holy wise men meet,
At the Royal Infant's feet,
Offerings rich are made by them,
To the star of Bethlehem.

Joyful let us quickly rise,
Still the signal's in the skies,
David's rod of Jesse's stem,
Is the star of Bethlehem.

BEHOLD, I bring you glad tidings of joy,
which shall be to all people. For unto you
is born this day in the city of David a Saviour,
which is Christ the Lord. And this shall be a
sign unto you : Ye shall find the babe wrapped
in swaddling clothes lying in a manger. And
suddenly there was with the angel a multitude
of the heavenly host praising God, and saying
Glory to God in the highest, and on earth
peace good-will toward men. Hallelujah, let
us sing, let us praise our God with hallelujah.

BEHOLD the splendour hear the shout,
Heaven opens, angels usher out.
And throng the northern sky.
Shepherds be glad he comes with peace,
Not wrath, but universal grace,
To bless each distant clime.

Shepherds heard the joyful sound,
Who watch'd their flocks upon the ground,
In dark and dreary night.
They left their flocks and herds behind,
Their Lord and Saviour for to find,
Led by a star of night.

See heaven's great heir a virgin's son
Behold a manger is his throne,
And spotless he must die.
Yours is the guilt and his the pain,
His is the sorrow yours the gain
And let his praise be high.

AWAKE ye nations of the earth,
And celebrate our Saviour's birth,
With grateful hearts salute the morn
On which our Saviour Christ, was born.

The shining hosts on wings of love,
Flew swiftly from the courts above,
With acclamations drown the skies,
And seize the shepherds with surprise.

The heav'nly choir aloud did sing :—
"This day is born the Saviour King"
They swell their notes of praise again :—
"Glory to God, good will to men."

AWAKE with joyful strains of mirth,
To celebrate the morn,
That brings glad news of Jesus' birth,
And of a Saviour born.

In lofty hymns your voices raise,
His mighty name adore,
And send your great Redeemer's praise
With shouts of joy therefore.

To thy great name, blest three in one,
Eternal praise belong!
Let heavenly angels join the throng,
And help to join our song.

BEHOLD a virgin shall conceive and bear
a Son, and shall call his name Immanuel,
God with us. Where is he that is born King
of the Jews ? for we have seen his star in the
east and are come to worship him. He shall
be great, and the Lord God shall give him the
throne of his Father David, and he shall reign
for ever and ever.

WHILE shepherds watch'd their flocks by
All seated on the ground, [night,
The Angel of the Lord came down,
And glory shone around.

Fear not said he, for mighty dread
Had seiz'd their troubled minds,
Glad tidings of great joy I bring
To you and all mankind.

To you in David's town, this day
Is born of David's line,
The Saviour, who is Christ the Lord,—
And this shall be the sign:

The heav'nly babe you there shall find
To human view display'd,
All meanly wrap'd in swaddling bands,
And in a manger laid.

Thus spake the seraph, and forthwith
Appear'd a shining throng
Of angels, praising God, and thus
Address'd their joyful song.—

"All glory be to God on high,
And to the earth be peace ;
Good-will henceforth from heav'n to men
Begin, and never cease."

STAR of the east, whose beacon light
A gleam on Bethlehem threw,
And thither by that wonderous sight
Arabia's sages drew.

On thee in thought we love to gaze
In western climes afar,
And think on thy mysterious rays,
Thou lovely eastern star.

Hail, thou, whose silvery radiance led,
Those Magian chiefs to bring
Their choicest gifts, in worship spread
Before Judea's King.

That glorious sun, whose harbinger
Thy light was made to shine,
And like the pillar'd flame to bear
Aloft salvation's sign:

Hail, thou, appointed to adorn
The rising King of heaven,
The promis'd child to Judah born,
The son to Israel given ;

In whom the peaceful Empire seal'd
Should more and more increase ;
In him, the mighty God reveal'd,
In him the Prince of Peace.

SEE they come a glorious army.
Down the bright celestial road,
Shouts seraphic now inspire me,
Fill my soul with love abroad,
Lo ! ten thousand,
All proclaim the new-born God.

Peace, good-will to men are given,
Hosts triumphant about awhile,
Son of man is come from heaven,
Earth receives the promised child.
His appearance,
Humble, lowly, meek and mild.

Now glory to the heaven born son,
And praised be his name,
All glory to the Three in One,
All honour to the same.

Printed by R. Woolcock, Helston, who is Agent for Whelpton's
celebrated Purifying and Stomach Pills; also for Kaye's far-famed
Pills. A Box of either of the above sent free on receipt of 13 Post-
age Stamps, to any Address. Half Box of Do. for 8 Stamps.
Printing of every description executed at the lowest prices.

most significant difference is in the Warmington publication where two extra bars are inserted just before the end to produce a minor cadence before resolving to the major as usual. It also has only three verses which are the ones most often sung today.

The 'Star of Bethlehem' was also carried to other parts of the world and we find it again appearing in Kadina, Australia in a collection by Joseph Glasson entitled *Twenty Six Celebrated Cornish Carols* 1927. It also travelled to America and is still sung in California's Grass Valley. There is a reference to Cornish miners working in the quick-silver mines in Almaden, California too:

> 'Besides singing in the mines, the Cornish miners would sing door to door beginning a week before Christmas. They sang songs popular in Cornwall, where they immigrated from, such as Lo the Eastern Sages Rise, Hark What Music Fills Creation, as well as the better known Hark! The Herald Angels Sing. Afterwards, they would visit with the residents and share saffron cake and tea'. (*Almaden Times*, December 22, 2005)

In 1929 it appears in Dunstan's collection where he states that it was: 'formerly very popular in the parishes of St Agnes, Mithian and Perranzabuloe and is still sung there'. His version comes from manuscripts dated 1840-50, but he does not say from where he obtained it. In the Padstow collection *Strike Sound*, in 1971 they describe it as a 'West Cornwall Tune'. Kenneth Pelmear, in 1982 has a version which looks like an amalgamation of several of the older manuscripts and adds that it is well known on the Isles of Scilly too!

Various carol covers of Stephen Nicholas' (1865-1927)

Nowadays most people in Cornwall attribute it to Stephen Nicholas (1865-1927) as it was printed by Sidney James in a collection of four of his carols around the 1960s 'from the original blocks'. There were several reprints of this collection, and while it has been suggested that he merely arranged this carol others dismiss the suggestion. Nicholas remains an important composer from Redruth, his most well-known carols today being 'The Star of Jacob' and 'What Heavenly Music'. He was born in North Country, near Redruth, and was a self-taught musician who became the choirmaster and organist at the Primitive Methodist chapel in Plain-an-Gwarry in Redruth. He emigrated to South Africa to join Robert Heath there. Stephen Nicholas was also a piano-tuner and eventually ran his own music shop for many years at West End in Redruth. According to the notes in one of the reprints of the Sidney James collection 'he was probably the first trader to sell records and gave concerts on Saturday nights which were a feature at that time'. His son, Charles, became the Musical Director of the Redruth Choral Society (begun by Heath) in 1931 until his death in 1961.

Our recording, from St Just Feast, has four verses and is similar to Nicholas' version. On our travels we also heard the Warmington arrangement on several occasions and even in Polperro, a more modern arrangement by Maddern-Williams, also sung at Boscastle.

St Just Feast is at the beginning of November and this heralds the start of the carol season. They always sing the 'top three': 'Hark the Glad Sound', 'Lyngham' and 'Star of Bethlehem' amongst the usual pub favourites. Over two hundred singers come together for this event from all over Cornwall and it is hosted by the Cape Cornwall Singers. In our previous book *Shout Kernow* we describe the Feast in more detail and actually show the Cape Cornwall Singers in action on our cover.

**Star of Bethlehem (Lo The Eastern) SAMUEL STANLEY (circa1803), words
JEHOIADA BREWER (circa 1790) with words of the 3 most common verses**

CD 2 Track 4

Lo! The East-ern Sa - ges rise At a sig - nal in the skies, Bright-er
Ba-laam's my-stic words ap - pear, Full of light di - vine-ly clear, And the
Joy - ful let us quick-ly rise, Still the sig-nal's in the skies. Da - vid's

than the bright-est gem, Bright - er
im - port wrapped in them, And the
rod of Jes - se's stem, Da - vid's

'Tis the Star of Beth - le - hem,

than the bright - est gem, 'Tis the Star of Beth - le - hem.
im - port wrapped in them, 'Tis the Star of Beth - le - hem.
rod of Jes - se's stem, 'Tis the Star of Beth - le - hem.

Star of Bethlehem (Lo the Eastern)
As sung at The Kings Arms, St Just on Feast Day 2012

1. Lo! The eastern sages rise
At a signal in the skies
Brighter than the brightest gem,
'Tis the Star of Bethlehem!

2. Balaam's mystic words appear
Full of light, divinely clear
And the import wrapped in them,
'Tis the Star of Bethlehem!

3. Rocks and deserts can't impede
On they press, no aid they need
Day and night a guide to them,
'Tis the Star of Bethlehem!

4. Joyful let us quickly rise!
Still the signal's in the skies
David's rod of Jesse's stem,
'Tis the Star of Bethlehem!

Also sung elsewhere:
Now the Holy Wise Men meet
At the Royal Infant's feet
Offerings rich and made by them,
To the Star of Bethlehem!

While Shepherds Watched

While Sheps!
(Brenda Wootton, *Pantomime Stew*, 1994)

The elders of the chapel sat the first week in December
To decide the Christmas music for to please each chapel member.

Jan Stone was there, his hair all combed, most faithful of all fellows,
The chapel organ wouldn't play without Jan – he pumped the bellows.

The minister was somewhat new – determined but polite,
'The first, I think,' he ventured, 'could it not be Silent Night?'

' 'Ow can 'ee start with that at all?' – Jan couldn't keep his scorn in,
'We can't go baalin' Silent Night first thing on Christmas mornin'!'

Brightest and Best was mooted then, and In Royal David's City,
But Jan demurred and told them all he didn't think it fitty.

'While Sheps is always how we start – I think I ought to knaw –
I've pumped they bellows forty year!' – they all agreed it so.

The preacher called for order; he certainly had spirit –
Suggested one in Latin (for he'd never heard of Merritt).

Someone garmed out Lo He Comes, another Hark the Glad,
Another – Star of Bethlehem – but Jan was getting mad.

His face was red… his feet was firm, upon the altar steps…
'You lot can sing just what you like – I'm going to pump While Sheps!'

Brenda Wootton (1928-1994), the well-known Cornish singer and poet

In the notes from the book, *Pantomime Stew*, Brenda Wooton's daughter, Sue, recalls singing carols in the car: *'Brenda had a wonderful store of old tunes and Methodist hymns; we prided ourselves at one time of being able to sing ten different versions of While Sheps'*. We also liked Vic Legg's assertion that: *'While Shepherds has got 55,023 versions in Cornwall alone!'*

Dunstan says 'Probably no Christmas carol or hymn ever written has had so many settings ... of Cornish settings of the words, over twenty have been long familiar to me or recently submitted to my notice'.

Through our research, we have found thirty-four versions known in Cornwall, either sung or talked about or in Cornish publications. According to some, there are over three hundred known versions in Britain. Why so many? For more details see the main introduction but, after the Restoration in the 1700s, the Church of England decreed it was the only carol to be sung, because the words followed closely to what was written in the Bible. It is based on the Gospel text of the Christmas story as the shepherds heard it, Luke 2: 8-14. It was then able to be disseminated across the country along with the *Book of Common Prayer*. Other carols which had roots in folk music were considered too secular at this time. According to Routley 'the multiplicity of settings is the natural result of the carol-famine [due to the Puritan suppression] and the eagerness with which folk would welcome anything that looked like a carol that had the authentic touch about it.'

Another reason for its popularity is because it is written in common or ballad meter so it fits many tunes; also in an age where few could read, a set of words that could be used with a variety of tunes was very useful.

The words are by Nahum Tate, who was born in Dublin in 1652 and died in Southwark in 1715, while living at Suffolk House, a refuge for debtors in London, probably as a result of alcoholism. Tate was primarily a poet and playwright, and was Poet Laureate in 1692. The carol was first published in 1700, in a supplement to the *New Version of the Psalms* by Tate and Nicholas Brady; this became the standard Psalter of the Church of England. 'Tate's straightforward telling of the nativity story is an example of paraphrasing at its best: poetry that conveys the text well without undue liberties or additions and is easy to understand and sing'. (www.hymnary.org)

Davies Gilbert also published a version of 'While Shepherds Watched', interestingly it is in the minor key and is in 3/2 time, both unusual for the carol hymns of this time. He describes it as a psalm tune and dates from 1724.

Most people will have sung these words to a tune called 'Winchester Old', by an unknown composer, to which it was set in *Hymns Ancient and Modern* (1861). In the mid-1800s, in an effort to standardise hymn singing by the Oxford Movement, this book became the standard hymn book for the Church of England, and many of the older tunes were discouraged and lost. In the dissenting Churches many of these tunes continued to be sung and found their way into the more secular places, in homes, streets and pubs, and as Cornwall has always had a strong Methodist tradition many of these versions would have been retained.

What follows is a selection of these found on our travels. Please see Appendix D, for a more comprehensive list.

While Shepherds Watched
(Nahum Tate)

1. While shepherds watched their flocks by night
All seated on the ground
The angel of the Lord came down
And glory shone around

2. Fear not said he (for mighty dread
Had seized their troubled minds)
Glad tidings of great joy I bring
To you and all mankind

3. To you in David's town this day
Is born of David's line
A saviour who is Christ the Lord
And this shall be the sign

4. The heavenly babe you there shall find
To human view displayed
All meanly wrapped in swaddling bands
And in a manger laid

5. Thus spake the seraph and forthwith
Appeared a shining throng
Of angels praising God who thus
Addressed their joyful song

6. All glory be to God on high
And to the earth be peace
Goodwill henceforth from heaven to men
Begin and never cease.

Bolingey version

One evening in early December 2015 we headed the short distance to Bridge Chapel near Portreath for their annual carol concert, where we would be singing with the Red River Singers, along with Tereba Nessa and Keur Heb Hanow. Tereba Nessa introduced a carol they were about to sing as the St Day version of 'While Shepherds Watched'. Sally was very excited to hear this as she wasn't aware of one from her home town. As they started to sing it, she thought, I know this! Then it dawned on her, it was one that we sang and knew as the Bolingey version!

So – Bolingey or St Day? Tereba Nessa told us that they knew it as St Day, as they had found a manuscript in Bridge Chapel that had been printed in Butte, Montana, in 1913 and was attributed to R. Rowe, St Day Handwritten at the top were the words 'Wesley Choir, St Day'. However, the Red River Singers had been singing this version for a couple of years, calling it Bolingey, after we had heard some of our own singers from Perranporth singing it. Chris Miners and Chris Easton both knew it as having been sung at Bolingey Chapel. It is also known in Polperro, where they call the tune 'Mount Zion'!

In Heath's two books of Cornish carols there are half a dozen or so carols attributed to W. Eade, one of the many Redruth composers of the time. In the first book, printed in 1889, this tune appears as 'What Melody', written by Eade. It also appears in Barnicoat's book of Tregony Manuscripts as 'What Melody'. Even so, it seems to have had a long history in Bolingey. Dunstan calls it 'Bolingey' and says this:

> 'William Borlase, who was born about 1860 and was brought up at Penwartha in Perranzabuloe, treasured the music used locally when singing this old and well known carol … He recalled how, in the last century [1800s] in Bolingey Chapel on Christmas morning, the Wesleyans were joined by their Church of England friends for the purpose of singing carols. The Bolingey tune for While Shepherds was always used. It was also used in a special broadcast of carols from Truro Cathedral some years ago.'

So – Bolingey or St Day? Polperro or Tregony?– no Redruth!

Butte, Montana, was opened up with mining for gold and silver, but later copper was discovered leading to huge numbers of Cornish miners heading that way for work. There are many reports in local newspapers of the late nineteenth and early and mid twentieth centuries following the exploits and lives of the many Cornish men and women abroad. Some of these, from *The Cornishman* between 1898 and 1909, tell us of the Cornish choirs in Butte and Centreville, Montana. One such article tells us that they sang 'Arise and Hail', 'Hark, Hark', and 'While Shepherds Watched' in Centreville's main thoroughfare on Christmas Eve. All these articles extol the wonderful singing of the Cornish carols carried from far off shores.

Linda, wife of Chris Miners, and also cousin to Chris Easton, gave us a connection between Bolingey and Butte. Linda told us about her great-aunt Bessie, Elizabeth Jane Inch who was born at Peniel, Penwartha in1893. Bessie's father was blinded in Chile,

but went on to run a coal business in Perranporth. Family life revolved around Bolingey Chapel and Bessie, who was a good singer, often sang solos and was a member of Perranporth and District Choral Society. Shortly after her marriage, she and her new husband Stanley, moved to Butte, Montana, where Stanley, a miner, found work. Whilst there, according to family history, she sang on the radio. Following the deaths of her husband from silicosis, and two of her children, she returned to Cornwall. She later remarried and settled in Goonhavern. Her new husband, Fred, was the founder of Goonhavern Banjo Band and their living room was always full of instruments including a grand piano. Bessie died in 1973. Coincidentally, Hilary's mother-in-law, Mary Veale played with the Banjo Band in the 1950s.

Chris Miners told us they sang this carol in Bolingey every Christmas until recently and we had hoped to record it there. However this was not to be and we used the recording of the Red Rivers singing at Bridge Chapel featuring both the Chris's! Another lovely version of the carol is on the Perraners CD of 2006, *A Seagull in a Pear Tree*.

Red River Singers at Bridge Chapel, 2016, with Chris Miners and Chris Easton on the back row, far left

Bolingey version, EADE arr. I.Marshall

As sung at the Bridge Chapel Concert by the Red River Singers, 2016 (Words on p.131)

CD 2 Track 5

Boscastle Jack

'They would want you to sing it again, and at the end they would say, "just like a horgan!"' (Roger Nicholls)

On a dark Tuesday night in early December 2016, we travelled up to Boscastle where Sally had lived until she was twelve, and where she still has family. There we met up with Roger Nicholls, MD of the Boscastle Buoys, on their usual singing night in the Napoleon Inn, a beautiful early seventeenth century, Grade II-listed pub. We were greeted with great friendliness, and Sally even met a 'Cornish cousin' – a man related by marriage to her brother-in-law!

We had made the journey up to hear 'Boscastle Jack', one of North Cornwall's many versions of 'While Shepherds Watched'. Roger Nicholls told us: *'I've been singing it ever since I was a kid. They would sing carols around the Camelford area to raise money for Cancer Research, they don't walk around and sing any more, although there's still a few of them left that will sing a few carols. When I was about thirteen or fourteen, about thirty years ago, my Dad would take me along, and we would walk around Camelford and up around Tregoodwell singing these local carols'.*

As well as 'Boscastle Jack', Roger knows of a number of other, local versions of 'While Shepherds Watched': *'There's a Tintagel one – "All Night" it's called; there's a Trewolder carol – "Glory Glory in the Highest"; we've got two in Boscastle – "Boscastle Jack" and Stewart Biddick remembers another Boscastle version, I've got to get these boys singing it!'*

Since at least the 1940s, carols have been sung on Boxing Day at the Masons Arms in

nearby Camelford, nowadays with Roger leading the singing, when 'Boscastle Jack' can still be heard.

This carol is named after Jack Davey, who was one of a musical family in Boscastle and was known as Boscastle Jack and Trapper Jack. He was trapper to Mr Ince of the Wellington Hotel. Arthur Biddick a local singer and musician who was also Roger's uncle, wrote down the tune from memory, we think in the 1970s.

The chorus clearly comes from the Sankey hymn 'We'll Never Say Goodbye', whilst the verse has some similarities to it. A part of Polperro's version of 'While Shepherds', ''Tis Christmas Time', is also reminiscent of the verse of this tune.

Above: Boscastle Buoys at Boscastle Harbour, 2006

Below: We'll Never Say Goodbye words; Heart Cheering Songs, 1899

The music for 'We'll Never Say Goodbye' was composed by John H. Tenney (1840-1918) and the words written by Anzentia Igene Perry Chapman (1849-1889). There is a fascinating story surrounding her writing of this hymn. It is said that Anzentia and her husband, Free Methodist preacher Edwin Willard Chapman, along with their four children travelled from their home in Michigan on an evangelical tour of Kansas, during which time their seven-year-old daughter, Eva, managed to swallow some coins. Five days later, Eva told them all that she was going to Heaven, and died. She was reputedly put into a glass-topped coffin in a cave, while her family continued with their tour. Later she was buried in Edna, Kansas. After the family returned home, Anzentia wrote this hymn in her daughter's memory.

The Boscastle Buoys got together in around 2005. Because one of their singers was given such great care at the end of his life by Cornwall Hospice Care's Mount Edgcumbe Hospice, the Boscastle Buoys pledged to raise money for them. They collect donations wherever they sing, and have donated over £25k to this worthy cause alone.

The arrangement of the tune in this book is the one as remembered by Arthur Biddick and is for mixed voices. Roger arranged the close harmony version you can hear on the CD for the Boscastle Buoys.

Boscastle Jack

As sung by the Boscastle Buoys at the Napoleon Inn, Boscastle, 2016 (Verse words on p. 131)

Chorus:
We'll never say goodbye in Heav'n,
We'll never say goodbye,
For in that land of joy and song,
We'll never say goodbye.

Boscastle Jack Traditional as remembered by ARTHUR BIDDICK

CD 2 Track 6

Lyngham

Our version comes from the singing on Boxing Day at the Tamar Inn in Calstock in East Cornwall. We wanted to record 'Lyngham' there as it was where Hilary had first learnt it: *'It was lovely to return to my home town and see so many people there I knew. The singing was raucously loud and the pub really noisy too! As I walked in they were singing 'Lyngham' but luckily they were happy to sing it again (and again!) An old family friend, Jack Spurr, was there who is in his 90s and I also managed to record him and my dad singing together which was quite special!'*

Hilary remembers learning this in the pub but actually her old music teacher from Callington School, Ian Marshall, used it in a carol concert at the school in 1973, so that is possibly where she first heard it. *'Every Boxing Day we would go down the Tamar to sing and this tradition continues to this day. My brother and I had heard stories from Jim Stacey, an old salmon fishing man, who taught us flashboat rowing, that backalong they'd blacken their faces with burnt cork and then go singing from house to house in the same old guising tradition recorded else-where. We carried on this tradition and found burnt cork far better than facepaints!'*

Henry James, a proper Calstonian Hilary knew when young, has fond memories from the early to mid 1920s of this guising which they called darkying:

'Groups of all ages would dress up in weird clothes, blacken their faces with burnt cork and thus greatly contribute to the lively evening with their music, dancing and carol singing. There was never any shortage of musicians … you name it, and they had to play it, English concertinas, melodeons, banjos, mouth organs, tin whistles, Jews-harps, saws, bones and spoons, the lot. By the 1930s I too was able to join in with them, with the piano accordion. The darkying activity was one of my boyhood delights. We youngsters received very little monetary reward for our carol singing but a very good share out of fruit, nuts, sweets, hot potatoes in their jackets, roast chestnuts and drinks, usually tea or lemonade. The custom was a happy affair and I recall, after meeting up with one of the adult groups, I wearily arrived at their usual base, The Steam Packet, weighed down camel-fashion with a huge jar of vintage cider, known in high-class darkying circles as "tonsil varnish". We school boys were never allowed into the bar, and had to be content with just a quick glimpse through open door or window. As the celebration progressed The Steam Packet pulsated to the old familiar rhythms and the house would wax hilarious at the antics and enthu-siasm of the revellers who simply bubbled over with good clean fun and merriment. After closing time the delightful cocktail of music, singing and sheer magic, would continue in Fore Street where many of the "non froth-blowing" fraternity would also be known to join in the revelry. Some of our best carol singing would be heard at this time, led by such men as George Cradick and company, whose rich Cornish voice flowed from one end of the street to the other. There the movements of the dancers and other performers were less restricted than in a crowded bar' (H. James, *Calstock History Society Newsletter*).

Nowadays, in Calstock, only a few of the Cornish carols are known, 'St Day' and Merritt's 'Hark the Glad Sound' are two of them, but there is a keenness with the singers there to learn more.

'Lyngham' is a fuguing tune with imitative lines and repetitions, a style which has remained so popular in Cornwall and although it is used for many hymns elsewhere it is indisputably tied to 'While Shepherds' in Cornwall, indeed it is often called the 'Cornish While Sheps' and there were not many places on our visits where it wasn't sung! In Troon *it is known as 'Whilst Shepherds New' and lends itself well to four part harmony.'* (D. Oates)

Most people would be surprised that it wasn't actually written in Cornwall but in the Midlands by Thomas Jarman and published in his book *Sacred Music*, around 1803.

Guising in Calstock, 1980s

He was born in 1776 in a village in Northamptonshire, and was a tailor. He joined the Baptist choir in his village and soon became the choirmaster.

> 'His natural taste for music, however, considerably interfered with his work, and he was frequently reduced to dire straits, from which only the extreme liberality of his publishers relieved him. He was a man of fine, commanding presence, but self-willed, and endowed with a considerable gift of irony, as choirs frequently found to their cost. Weston quotes from Kant that Jarman neglected his work and "this kept him poor and soured his temper"'. (Hymnary.org)

Jarman published a great deal of music, including over six hundred hymn tunes. This tune, 'Lyngham', is also popularly connected outside of Cornwall to the hymn

'Oh for a Thousand Tongues' by Wesley.

An example of how well the tune is known in Cornwall comes from Brian Oaten in Port Isaac:

'A year or so after the end of the Second World War, men in and around the village of Trebetherick, on the north coast of Cornwall, decided to build their own social club. A piece of land was given by a local farmer and a large, ex-army, wooden hut which probably dated from the First World War was acquired. As the summer progressed, during their spare time in the light evenings and at weekends, the men set about assembling the structure. One particular volunteer, Fred Tabb, devoted a lot of time

to helping with the construction. His mates were always perplexed, as he was endlessly whistling the same tune: While Shepherds Watched which is traditionally sung, all over Cornwall, to the tune Lyngham. When finally the building was ready, it was decided to call it The Lingham [sic] Club. Eventually it was sold and became a pub called Carpenters. Coincidentally, a new primary school for the parish at Rock was in the final stage of planning. The funds from the sale of the club were donated to the school to enable it to have a much larger assembly/sports hall. This is named The Lingham Hall and serves as a venue for local public activities, just as the Lingham Club had done, although you can't pop in for a swift half any more'.

Singers in the Tamar Inn, Calstock, 2016

Lyngham T.JARMAN (1776-1861) arr. based on I.Marshall's

As sung in Tamar Inn, Calstock, Boxing Day, 2016 (words on p.131)
CD 2 Track 7

While shep-herds watched their flo-cks by - night, all seat-ed on the ground, all sea- ted

While shep-herds watched their flocks by night, all sea- ted

While shep-herds watched their flo-cks by - night, all sea- ted

While shep-herds watched their flocks by night, all seat-ed on the ground, all sea- ted

on the ground, The ang-el of the lo - rd came down, And

on the ground, The ang-el of the lo - rd came down,

on the ground, The ang-el of the lord came down,

on the ground, The ang-el of the lo - rd came down, And glo-ryshone a

glo-ry shone a -round, and glo-ry shone a - round, and glo - ry shone a -round.

and glo-ry shone a -round, and glo - - ry shone a -round.

and glo-ry shone a - round, and glo - ry shone a -round.

round, and glo-ry shone a-round, and glo - ry, and glo - ry shone a -round.

Newlyn version

On our travels we heard this melody described as the Newlyn version of 'While Shepherds Watched' and we heard it sung by Mousehole Male Voice Choir at Paul Church. Their MD, Stephen Lawry, subsequently sent us their arrangement which was by Richard John Maddern Williams and on the manuscript it is just described as 'an old Cornish carol'. Maddern Williams conducted Mousehole Male Voice Choir from 1945-1954. Originally from Pendeen, he left to gain a Fellowship at the Royal College of Organists, then, when he retired from his post as assistant organist at Norwich Cathedral, he returned to Cornwall. He was also MD for Penzance Orchestra and Operatic Society and Pendeen MVC.

His style was described as being in marked contrast to many other Cornish choir leaders with his 'quiet style and modest authority'. Maddern Williams was not interested in competitive singing but broadcasting became a large part of the choir's output especially because of his friendship with the West of England BBC musical director Reginald Redman.

> 'The conductor was gifted in arranging music for four-part male voice singing, be it spirituals, folk-songs or choruses by classical composers. He published some arrangements of Christmas carols and it was a joy to turn up to practise his latest works.' (Bill Harvey, Choir member for nine years and a former chairman, *A Century of Song*, 2009)

These published carols probably helped the carol spread elsewhere, for we heard it at a concert by the Washaway West Gallery Choir at Pencarrow House where it was said that it is still sung at St Wenn each year. It is also known in the Boscastle area where Roger Nicholls has sung it with *'the Camelford lot since I was a kid'*. Also, Murray Collings, from the Polperro Fishermen's Choir, remembers singing 'Awake with Joy' and 'Star of Bethlehem', both arranged by Maddern Williams.

In December 2015 we travelled to hear the Mousehole MVC Carol Concert at Paul Church. It was very lovely to be at their annual concert and hear such great singing from the choir. This concert is eagerly anticipated every year and features a wealth of Cornish carols. The choir acknowledge their links with the past, from Davies Gilbert, through Methodism to the present day:

> 'Steve Lawry and the Mousehole Choir still follow on this worthy tradition. Carols such as Lo, He Comes an Infant Stranger, Hark the Glad Sound, Angelic Hosts are just some examples of wonderful Cornish carols that we sing in concert or in the pub. Our annual Christmas Concert will convince you that the work and dedication to the Cornish Carol by our forefathers and also by our wonderful Choir has all been worthwhile'. (Mousehole MVC website)

The Christmas carols have always been important to the choir from their birth in 1909 when 'a small group of Mousehole men – there were probably no more than ten in all – first got together to practise Christmas carols, in a loft above the fish-curing tanks. The first piece the choir rehearsed was Holly Berries, Bright Red and Gleaming, the words being chalked up on the net loft door. Willie Harvey told his daughter that, aged 16, he was the first man up the ladder. Imagine the primitive scene with a pile of nets in the corner and singing by the light of an oil lamp' (*A Century of Song*)

Mousehole is famed for its Christmas lights and the Choir combine with members of the Mousehole Methodist Church and singers from the community to form the Carolaire Choir for their switch-on. They then sing again for the traditional Tom Bawcock's Eve.

In 1970 the choir recorded an LP, *Cornish Christmas Carols*, which marked their Diamond Jubilee and 'preserved the traditional Christmas music sung by Mousehole men from generation to generation'. Then again they produced a CD in 2013 called Christmas with Mousehole 'to meet requests from Cornish Cousins around the world who want a taste of home'. This has the Pendeen version of While Shepherds Watched which their current MD, Stephen Lawry remembers learning as a child.

There is a delightful book called *A Century of Song – The Story of Mousehole and its Famed Male Voice Choir*, compiled and edited by Douglas Williams and from which we have taken some of our excerpts. It was written to celebrate 100 years of the choir's existence and is a great read.

Mousehole Male Voice Choir, Paul Church, 2015

While Shepherds Watched, Newlyn version TRADITIONAL arr. Maddern Williams *As sung by the Mousehole Male Voice Choir at Paul Church, December 2015 (words on p.131) CD 2 Track 8*

While shep - herds watch'd their flocks___ by night, All

seat - ed on___ the ground, The an - gel of the

Lord came down, And glo - ry shone___ a - round.

Two Pendeen versions and one from Treen

This version of 'While Shepherds' seems to be fairly well known in the Penwith area. We have heard of people singing it around Zennor as well as Penzance and Newlyn and presumably Pendeen too! Our written version of the tune is from Stephen Lawry, the MD for Mousehole MVC, who learnt it when young and arranged it for mixed voices for Govenek Choir then rearranged it for Mousehole MVC. They recorded it on their Christmas album: *Christmas with Mousehole* in 2013.

There are echoes of the song Ilkley Moor in the opening bar and this presumably led to the *Lincolnshire Echo* in 1926, writing that 'someone has claimed it as an old Cornish carol'. It is true that the tune for Ilkley Moor was originally a hymn written by Thomas Cook (1775-1859) of Canterbury published in 1805 and called 'Cranbook' and it is sung to 'While Shepherds Watched', but in Yorkshire!

On the night we went down to the Dock Inn in Penzance they sang three versions of 'While Shepherds': this Pendeen version, sung by the Pendeen Miner's Choir and one version from Treen.

In 1950, the *Western Morning News* announced that on the Monday before Christmas Pendeen MVC choir would broadcast, presumably on BBC Radio, 'A selection of Cornish Carols'.

Pendeen Miners choir

Of the Pendeen Miners' Choir version, one of the main singers at the Dock, Rick Williams, said: *'we got it off a reel-to-reel tape of a 78 rpm record, originally recorded in 1942 of the Pendeen Miner's Choir. Maddern Williams was in charge of the choir in those old recordings.*

I've asked several people if they know what happened to the Pendeen Miner's Choir manuscripts, some people have said they went to St Buryan. So I've asked people up St Buryan if they'd have a look and they couldn't turn anything up, other people thought they might be over Marazion, nothing over there. So I don't know what happened to them.'

Rick Williams used to sing with the Newlyn MVC: *'We used to sing "While Sheps"* [Treen version] *in Newlyn in the late seventies. They used to go to the Dolphin on Christmas Eve; my Dad suggested I might like to start going there at about the age of fifteen. Nobody had any sheets, they all knew the words, they all knew the parts, some of the best singers in Newlyn, in a square room facing each other which is just perfect, there might be a few stragglers in the small doorway listening. We used to call them the Wet Brigade – the ones that would go singing in the pub after a practice. Ken Northey, who used to conduct the choir when I was in it, had Maddern Williams' habit of making the basses sing really low and the tenors sing really high, he would squeeze as many notes out of you as he possibly could, which is a brilliant thing, but it's not easy. You listen to those Pendeen Miners' Choir tapes – they've got some beauty basses, and some really high* [tenors]. *And that's what Ken used to do'.*

We also heard this Treen version of 'While Shepherds Watched' at the Dock Inn and Rick recalls that Newlyn MVC *'used to do what we now call the Treen While Sheps back then. I've mentioned it to loads of people every Christmas since then "do you know this one?"* [Sings] *I'm always met with blank faces. It was Graham Kirkham, I think, who lent Steve Hall a CD, one of the Peter Kennedy things, and that reminded me. I hadn't dreamt it! And I reconstructed it from there'.*

The recording that Rick refers to was made by Peter Kennedy in 1956 at the Logan Rock Inn and features on a compilation called *Camborne Hill, Songs and Customs from Cornwall.* Kennedy actually records three different versions by 'John Chappelle and chorus' – 'Lyngham', 'Pendeen' and this Treen version.

Between Christmas and New Year, Hilary visited the Logan Rock at Treen to meet up with family and friends and join in with the Cadgwith Singers, who have been going over to sing there for over twenty years. Whilst there, her brother Will, introduced her to Lyn Batten who remembered the men singing the Treen version: *'Lewis and Ted Matthews, and there was another brother I think. I knew Ted. The old guy, Chappelle, would've been Teddy's grandad who lived in the house right next to the pub, John Chappelle.'*

Hilary then joined in with a small group which included her brother and Lyn who went out the back of the pub to have a go at it! Hopefully next Christmas there'll be a stronger representation there. All Glory be!

Pendeen version TRADITIONAL as remembered by S.Lawry

Version on recording is from the Dock Inn, December 2015 (Words on p.131)
CD 2 Track 9

Stithians version

'Music has long played a major role in the social life of Stithians. In the late 1800s there were choirs at St Stythians Parish Church, Hendra Methodist Chapel and Penmennor Methodist Chapel. There was also Dunstan's Drum and Fife Band during the First World War; its repertoire consisted of folk songs, patriotic war songs and Sankey Hymns.' (The Book of Stithians, 1999).

We went to hear the Stithians version of 'While Shepherds Watched' one evening in December 2015. There has been an annual carol concert with St Stythians Male Voice Choir, Stithians Ladies Choir and St Stythians Silver Band in the village hall for over thirty years. Before that time, singers had collected for charity as they sang carols around Stithians from before living memory; the band had also gone out playing carols. As local interest waned in coming out on a dark, cold night to hear the carols, it was decided to hold a joint carol service in the space between the school and the village hall. But the very first year, it poured with rain so everyone went in to the hall, and it's been inside ever since!

A choir has existed in Stithians intermittently since 1913, with a break during the First World War, starting up again in 1919. The choir ceased in 1926 but reformed again in 1947 and is still active today. Amongst their other recordings they have produced a series of five CDs of some seventy three Sankey hymns, along with Stithians Ladies Choir. The Ladies Choir was formed in 1966 by Sydney Bowden. St Stythians Silver Band originally formed in 1928, and, later, with Edgar Floyd as Musical Director they become one of Cornwall's leading bands.

St Stythians MVC, Stithians Ladies Choir, Carol concert, 2015

'It was the tradition for the men from the village to gather and go around houses singing carols at Christmas time and it was these men who formed the nucleus of the choir' (St Stythians MVC website)

Ken Downing, the current Musical Director of St Stythians Male Voice Choir told us: *As a child it was part of Christmas really, going around singing mainly Merritt, Nicholas and Warmington carols. At that time I was also in Stithians band, trombone, and of course they used to go around the village and the outlying areas playing carols, on several evenings and Christmas morning, we always played out Christmas morning up until lunch time outside of the pub, over the crossroads, and then down towards the mill. Mr Harold Phillips used to own the mill there then. He would have the band down there and give them a drink for Christmas. The singers just went around the village over a couple of nights. When the Old Vicarage was going, they invited us back there to finish, and they put on a drink and some mince pies. Sometimes we went in to the Seven Stars, but we didn't go to people's houses like the band. The band would be invited, especially on Christmas morning. The band played Merritt's carols under the light of Tilley lanterns, carried on wooden posts, so they could see to play. They're still playing Merritt; I think they sound lovely with a band playing them.'*

The Stithians version of 'While Shepherds Watched' was composed by Lewis H. Pascoe, between 1905-10, and is still sung each Christmas in Stithians. Pascoe was the organist of the Stithians Penmennor Methodist Church from 1903-44. Ken Downing is fairly sure that he died in July 1944, aged 59, and is buried, along with his wife, in Stithians' churchyard.

Sidney Bowden, was the organist and choirmaster of Penmennor Chapel following Lewis Pascoe, and was also the conductor of the Male Voice Choir. In the early eighties Bowden retired as conductor but told Ken Downing, *'here's some copies of Lewis's carol,*

look after it, because if it get lost, it'll be gone, this is all we got.'

Ken Downing says: 'I think seeing as we've got this Stithians carol, I want to try and keep it going! It's very similar to a Merritt carol. It's that style. You've got that repeated line all the time.' It is interesting to note that Pascoe wrote the carol in 1905 just two years before Merritt died, and may have been influenced by Merritt's style.

Ken Downing is the choir's longest serving member having joined them in November 1965, just a month short of his fifteenth birthday; he has sung in every section. Whilst a pupil at Trewirgie School, Redruth, Ken joined the school band and a well-known local brass teacher, Frank Moore, used to come in every Friday. Another member at that time was Roy Trelease who is now the current MD of Carharrack and St Day Silver Band, who you can hear on our recording of the 'St Day Carol'.

In 1983 Sidney Bowden retired as conductor of the choir, having been there since 1947, and after a short spell of being led by David Eastbourne, Downing took over the baton in 1986, taking them to sing at Stithians Show as his first outing in that capacity.

Ken Downing was pleased that we had come to record the carol but added: 'This is nearly left too late, there's nobody I can go to … there's several a little bit older than me that have been in Stithians village all their life and they know of him [Lewis Pascoe], just like I've heard of him. I didn't know him, obviously, but of course, everybody that really knew him, they would be a hundred or so. It's more than likely when my time come finishing with the choir that'll stop [singing Pascoe's carol], because a lot of people will say, "Oh, we don't want to sing that old thing!"'

Let's hope that he's wrong!

Above: Stithians UMFC Choir on steps of Chapel, 1901, Lewis Pascoe on front right

Opposite: The Logan Rock Inn, Treen, 2017, where the Treen version of While Shepherds Watched was recorded

Stithians version LEWIS H. PASCOE (circa 1907)

As sung at Stithians Village Hall, by St Stythians MVC & Stithians Ladies Choir, December 2015 (Words on p.131)
CD 2 Track 10

While shep-herds watch'd their flocks by night, All seat-ed on the ground, all seat-ed on the ground, all seat-ed on the ground, The an-gel

[Organ Ped.]

of the Lord came down, the an-gel of the Lord came down, the an-gel of the Lord came down, And glo-ry shone a-round, and glo-ry shone a-round, and

And glo-ry shone a-round, and

round, a-round, and glo-ry shone a-round.

glo-ry shone a-round,

'Tis Christmas Time

One of our early trips to record carols was a visit to the Polperro Fishermen's Choir. They sang a version of 'While Shepherds Watched' called ''Tis Christmas Time', that they've 'always sung' there. The verse has similarities to another version known as 'Boscastle Jack' but the chorus is quite different and feels like a much newer addition.

In July 2017 Polperro Fishermen's Choir had a concert where they celebrated the fact that one of their members, Murray Collings, had been a part of the choir for an amazing 65 years. When we talked to him he reckoned that over those years he'd sung four or five versions of 'While Shepherds Watched'; *'our version, Lyngham, Mount Zion, the traditional Church one and there was another one, Sweet Chiming Bells'*. His comment 'the traditional church one' is interesting – he goes on later to say: *'The Church was very much the normal, set carols but the Chapel was more flexible, they had adaptations of carols and things like that. The Methodists retained far more traditional, local stuff than anybody else'*. He also explained how he felt the carols were spread around: *'The fishing community would go and fish out of Newlyn, now that could be Christmas, and one lot would bring their version, others would have their version, and that's how it was. They would take it with them if they could read; my grandfather could sign his name, that's all he could do. His knowledge was up there!'* [Tapping his head]

The Choir has grown recently and is now forty strong and, according to Murray, a lot of it is down to the Wreckers, a sub-group of the choir, *'they like this afterglow, going in the pub and having a sing-song'*, which has attracted new members to the choir.

Murray told us some background about the choir which started around 1923: *'It started off with Eva Cloak who was the Chapel organist, her husband Jimmy Cloak was an ex-*

Polperro Fishermen's Choir rehearsing in Polperro chapel, 2015. Murray Collings front row on right

Mevagissey man, Cloaks were quite a family over Mevagissey. Anyway she formed what was called a Fishermen's Choir. You see Eva Cloak came from a fishing family in Polperro. Jimmy Cloak's boat was The White Heather, fished out of Polperro. I went in as a fifteen year old and sat by Jimmy, in the bass section. So I sang bass from that time forward. When I first joined the choir, there were five youngsters went in the same time. You'd have a hell of a job finding five youngsters now going in, they just aren't interested, but, well I suppose there were less other attractions, so you went into the choir and immediately you had a wider range of friends. I got a lot of joy out of it. It wasn't all fishermen there were all these allied trades, I was a carpenter by trade, and there were lots of other people that were involved in the choir from farmers right throughout, which was good really. When I first joined the choir, we didn't sing anything but hymns. Some would be anthems but they would be all religious'.

He then went on to talk about the carol singing: *'Christmas we always went carol singing. We went out touring the week before Christmas, and usually a farmer, who perhaps was in the choir or allied, would lay on a bun-fight time we finished, so we'd all end up there, perhaps sing there, course we had cars then. Sometimes we would go at Christmas to Polruan, go around there singing, or go to Looe and sing. But now we go around to the Old People's Homes. They always ended up back at the harbour, which would be midnight, and they would sing a piece called Welcome To the New Born Christ, this was to welcome the baby as you can imagine. I've never heard of anybody else doing that sort of thing. But it's not sung anymore'.*

We heard a version of 'Welcome' at Pencarrow sung by the Washaway Gallery Choir and it was from the Heath collection, collected from a Mrs Berry of Chacewater – could it be the same 'Welcome'?

They also used to sing a carol called 'Behold': *'We don't sing it now, but I have sung this one all me life, in a sense. God knows where it came from, its origins. Somewhere there may be a proper written version of it, but by the same token it might be purely local. In my time it was always hand-written, none of it was ever a professional job. The old choir, we used to sing it in three parts instead of four'.*

When interviewing Peter Meanwell from the Washaway Gallery choir he showed us a really old handwritten music book from over one hundred and fifty years ago which had this carol in it and told us it was composed by Thomas Jarman (of 'Lyngham' fame).

Murray also sang a fragment of one called 'Bethlehem's Star': *'Glorious morning we hail thy return, bringing glad tidings, the Saviour is born! Heralds shall waft the glad news from afar… Sweet Bethlehem Star'.*

There is a description in J. Couch's *History of Polperro* from 1871 of the carols sung there: 'On Christmas Eve the mirth begins, when the mock or yule-log is lighted; it may be from a portion saved from last year's fire. In farmhouses the husbandmen and neighbours come in about evening and spend some hours in singing carols, clearing their voices with occasional draughts of cider. The travelling hawker has been around with his penny broad-sheet where The First Good Joy Our Mary Had, As I Sat on a Sunny Bank, and God Rest You Merry Gentlemen are in company with As Shepherds Watched Their Flocks by Night, Kirke White's Star of Bethlehem and others which seem out of place in such almost ludicrous company'.

The distinction between broadsheet/folk carols and carol hymns is clearly seen here as described in our introduction on the history of carols. Henry Kirke White 1785-1806

Two manuscripts of Behold, one from Polperro, one from Peter Meanwell's collection

was a poet and hymn writer from Nottingham and his carol 'Star of Bethlehem' is still sung around Sheffield.

Murray recalled the practice of guising in Polperro: '*Now the old choir, as I refer to it before the war, they walked around the locality, they would go out and sing around to different farmhouses, cottages and what-have-you, blacked-up. They used to call it Darky Dancing. It was a disguise. We never did that. I've always heard that they got back to the village in the early hours of the morning, but men worked right up till Christmas then! I suppose it was their only release, singing was their entertainment*'.

Couch refers to this tradition back in 1871: 'In town the family, flocking round the mock are interrupted by the cheerfully tolerated intrusion of the "Goosey-Dancers". The boys and girls rifle their parents' wardrobes of old gowns and coats, and disguise themselves, their mien and speech, so cleverly that it is impossible to recognise them. They are allowed, and are not slow to take, the large amount of licence which the season warrants; for it is considered a mark of churlish disposition to take offence at anything they do or say. Accordingly they enter without ceremony, dance, sing and carry on an extemporaneous dialogue well spiced with native wit. After tasting, unasked perhaps, whatever may be on the table, they beg some money to make merry with. The children are much amused, and the mummers leave with a benediction.'

The Polperro Fishermen's Choir had a particular outfit: '*When I first joined you'd have a pair of grey trousers, could be many shades, and you'd 'ave the jersey which fishermen wore to work, or they had a best one. My mother worked in a general dealers in the village and they would allowance out so many ounces of wool to knitters who would knit the guernseys, knit-frock or whatever you like to call it. There is a photo of my grandfather in a book, with a set of whiskers, James Curtis. Seeds and Bars I think was Polperro.*'

Murray is referring to the jumpers specially knitted for fishermen; the term knit-frock was peculiar to Polperro. In the Rowett Institute at Polperro there is a panel of photographs from the 1850s by Lewis Harding depicting portraits of eighty two fisher-

men each wearing a knit-frock with around fifteen wearing the Seeds and Bars pattern Murray describes. In 1979 Mary Wright published a book called *Cornish Guernseys and Knit-Frocks* and it is this book Murray mentions.

There is a photo of the Choir from the Twenties: *'In the photo the men are all wearing knit frocks, the ones they worked in. 1920 something. On the back of the photo – this is the story, one of the choir members went to America and was sent out this picture, and he put a name to everybody that was in the choir. Dick Joliffe was the local preacher, and very often when we was more religious as a choir, he would MC the do. They had him on the one-off Polperro version of Songs of Praise. The photo came back from America with all the names he had put on. Gerald Mark would be a brother, to him. His ancestor was the last smuggler shot!'*

Funnily enough Sally was in the process of knitting a Bude version of a knit-frock for her brother which had to be put on hold whilst this book was being written. Hopefully it is now finished!

Polperro fishermen wearing knit-frocks, c.1880, with Murray Collings's grandfather James Curtis on the right

'Tis Christmas Time

As sung at Polperro Chapel, by the Polperro Fishermen's Choir, December 2015
(Verse Words on p.131)

Chorus
'Tis Christmas time, the Angel's song is sounding,
'Tis Christmas time, their notes are still resounding,
And all along the way of life
In hope and struggle, toil and strife,
We soon shall hear the Angels sing:
'Fear thou not for Christ is king'

'Tis Christmas Time TRADITIONAL

CD 2 Track 11

HARK! THE GLAD SOUND OF CORNISH CAROLS

Chorus

'Tis Christ - mas time,_____ 'Tis

'Tis Christ - mas time,_____ the an - gel's song_ is sound - ing, 'Tis

'Tis Christ - mas time, the an - gel's song is sound - ing,

'Tis Christ - mas time, the an - gel's song is sound - ing,

Christ - mas time,_____

Christ - mas time,_____ their notes_ are still re - sound - ing,

'Tis Christ - mas time, their notes are still re - sound - ing,

'Tis Christ - mas time, their notes are still re - sound - ing,

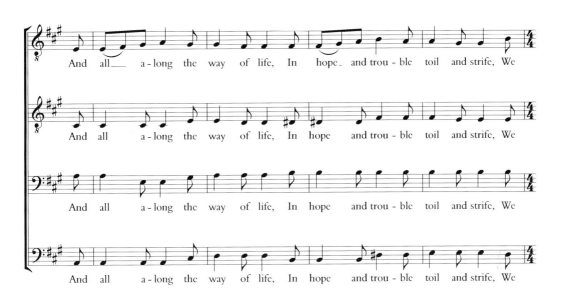

Wassails and Winter Festivals

Upon New Year's Eve (excerpt)
Sir Arthur Thomas Quiller-Couch (1863-1944)

Now winds of winter glue
Their tears upon the thorn,
And earth has voices few,
And those forlorn.

And 'tis our solemn night
When maidens sand the porch
And play at Jack 's Alight
With burning torch,

Or cards, or Kiss i' the Ring –
While ashen faggots blaze,
And late wassailers sing
In miry ways.

(From *The Oxford Book of Victorian Verse*, 1922)

The original meaning of wassail is retained in phrases such as 'here's health' or 'here's to you' and wassail customs have always been associated with drinking to health. The Saxon words Waes Hael, meaning 'be whole', are recorded as a toast by Geoffrey of Monmouth in *History of the Kings of Britain* in approximately 1150, and by the time of Henry VII wassailing had become a court function and despite its pagan origin, the wassail bowl had a place among monastic festivities. The tradition of frightening evil spirits from orchards is recorded in medieval times, however in Cornwall it would seem that a different form has been retained. John Stephens was familiar with wassailing in his native town of Bodmin and through the Old Cornwall Society he realised

there were other versions around Cornwall which he considered were 'nearing extinction' and so decided to research into them. He wrote an article for *Old Cornwall* in 1932 entitled 'Cornish Wassailing' and even asked Quiller-Couch for his recollections, as he too was from Bodmin. John Stephens said that 'in many parts of England orchards, fields and cattle were wassailed as well as persons but all evidence in the Duchy relates to the simple custom of parties of men or boys going around at Christmas and the New Year singing some version of the Wassail song – a song of two or four line verses and a chorus'. However in an article for the *Western Morning News* by A. A. Clinnick in December 1925, entitled 'Days of Wassailing and Carolling', it describes:

> 'The custom "wassailing" the apple trees in the Duchy on the eve of Twelfth day was practiced in Cornwall as well as in Devon but in the Duchy it was customary to procure a wild crab apple to hang up over the hearth to please the brownie who belonged to the house before making use of the wassail bowl'.

The house-to-house form of wassailing was once commonly observed in Devon – many references are given in the verses of Robert Herrick, who was the Vicar of Dean Prior at Totnes in the 17th century. John Stephens believed that the custom would have been brought across the Tamar (although we have found no evidence of it occurring in East or North Cornwall, see the revived Cotehele Wassail). He also assumed that, being an Anglo Saxon custom, it was not adopted by Cornish speakers and that therefore there is no record of it in West Cornwall. He was obviously not aware of the traditions in Redruth and the Lizard.

Wassailing has always been associated with Christmas and the New Year and was

Grampound Wassailers and bowl, from left to right Henry Brown, William Luke, Richard Mannell, 1930

often continued until Twelfth Night. In some places this is the night it is now tradition-ally held (as with the Bodmin Wassail). 'Wassail parties were usually three to half-a-dozen in number, often the same men following on from year to year over a long period'. (John Stephens)

All the Cornish wassail songs have their local variations in words and music, but they seem to derive from one common stock which singers have adapted over the years and added verses to suit their own situation. The Cornish versions differ from the five English examples given in the *Oxford Book of Carols,* although there are similarities in a few verses. The one with words most in keeping with the Cornish version was col-lected by A. L. Lloyd from a Phil Tanner before he died in a Gower Workhouse in 1947. One thing the wassails have in common is that they survived through oral tradition. John Stephens says of his collecting 'in no single case have I been supplied with printed words, but only with verses written from memory, and all the tunes recovered have also been in memory-written manuscript'

In his article, Stephens says that he was only aware of wassails along the coast from Looe to Falmouth and inland around Bodmin, St Austell, Grampound and Truro. He says: 'At Penryn, where the Cornish Miracle Plays originated, the custom existed, and the word "Wassail" as Wassel actually occurs in the Cornish Passion Play'.

The Grampound version was sent to the collector, Baring-Gould by J. Barrett, of Lemon Street, Truro, around the turn of the twentieth century with the note: 'At last I am able to send you the Cornish Wassail song, which I promised you a twelvemonth a gone. Mr J. J. Mountford, the organist of St John's church has got the two versions of the music, one from the old man from whom I got the words, but I do not know from whence he obtained the other. Michael Nancarrow, from whom air and words were taken, is a native of Grampound and is now 73 years old. He has been singing the song for fifty years, and learnt it from Wm Griffin and Rd Darker, old men who have been dead near twenty years. The words I send have been known in this neighbourhood as the Grampound song, being distinct from the Tregoney and other versions.'

Baring-Gould also had a version from Fowey. The version from Truro was kept alive by an old man called Ben Little, a Truro cattle drover, 'who for 50 years without a break has wandered over Truro district at Christmas time from Boxing Day to Twelfth Night, visiting the chief county houses from Caerhays Castle to Flushing to sing his old was-sail song. His wooden bowl is made in the orthodox manner and truly he chants with his sons: 'Now we poor wassail boys are growing wary and old'. (A. A. Clinnick)

There is a photo of Ben Little accompanying the article by John Stephens, the cap-tion reads 'He is 87 years old and has toured parts of Cornwall singing Wassail songs for over 73 years. The bowl of apple wood here shown has been carried by him for over 62 years.'

Ralph Dunstan recorded a version from William Dunstan of Carnon Downs in 1912 which came from MSS and personal recollection. He describes it as being 'well-known in West Cornwall fifty or sixty years ago.'

In *Canow Kernow*, Inglis Gundry publishes a wassail sung by Joe Thomas in Constantine in 1956, recorded by Peter Kennedy. Mr Thomas describes how: 'back in old times any gang of chaps would go out on New Year's Eve and scour the countryside, go from farm to farm. They used to car' a bowl with 'em – anything like a basin would do. You'd fill'n up with cider or beer, then you'd drink around, fill'n up again.' He also remarks how he was 'out over Helford River one night wassailing – came home four o'clock in the morning.'

The wassail bowl has always had a prominent place in wassail customs – it *'was at one time a recognised institution in itself. The bowl maybe looked upon as a symbol of the custom's life.'* (John Stephens) They are not standardised to one pattern and can vary in size and shape but are generally made of wood although the type can vary; oak, ash, maple, apple and holly have all been used. The oldest specimens have even been made from Lignum Vitae. These trees are indigenous to the Caribbean and the northern coast of South America, and have been exported to Europe since the beginning of the 16th century. Its wood was once very important due to its extraordinary combination of strength, toughness, and density. Each bowl has its own character, some with holes for sprigs of holly, bay or laurel.

At Grampound, John Stephens says 'the old bowl, which fell in pieces years ago through age, had holes down the inside, into which pegs were inserted. Each man drank down to his peg'. Interestingly the next bowl was discovered only a few years ago being used to keep an old ladies knitting in. J. Barrett, of Lemon Street, Truro, describes the use of the bowl there: 'The first three verses are usually sung outside the house and, before the fourth verse is sung, some liquor is supplied. The singers carry a bowl into which all liquor given is poured, and when they leave the home they usually carry some away in case they should meet anyone on their way to the next house. Should they do

*Grampound
Wassail Bowl*

Raffidy Dumitz Band at Degol Stul, 2017

so the ninth verse is sung; verses 10 and 11 are only sung on Twelfth Day:

9. Where you've had one hosget [Hogshead] we hope you'll get ten
To give us some cider when we come again.

10. The cattle's in stable, the corn's in the barn
A drop of good cider won't do us no harm.

11. We wish you a Merry Christmas and a Happy New Year
A-plenty of money and a cellar of beer'.

At Bodmin, even back in the 1930s the bowl was made of pottery as it is today. The drinks most commonly associated with the bowl are either cider or beer. However, this was more likely governed by 'means rather than taste, spiced wine became the wassail of the rich, beer and cider were the wassail of the many.' (J. Stephens)

There are many descriptions of the preparations of the cider wassail bowl; John Stephens describes one in his article: 'A bowl of cider was placed on the hearth before the fire; above it crab-apples were hung by strings attached to their stems, as these became thoroughly cooked they dropped their juice and pulp into the cider, pieces of toast, nutmeg and spices were added, the whole being whipped into a frothy white compound, sometimes called "lamb's-wool".'

The tradition of guising was also carried out at Christmas time around Cornwall known variously as Goosey-Dancing, Darkying or Mumming, we have included memories of this tradition from Polperro and Calstock. There are also many references in Cornwall to performances of the well known mummers play, St George and the Turkish Knight, starting with the lines 'Here comes I ...' which often included the character of Father Christmas. They are typically adapted to suit the locality and always performed in a rough and ready style. This idea of irreverent celebration is continued and revived by the Cornish Cultural Association and their band Raffidy Dumitz who also play for the Redruth Wassail, Degol Stul and at several other winter festivals but predominantly at Montol in Penzance for the Winter Solstice. Other Winter festivals are mentioned in this book such as Degol Stul, Picrous Eve and Tom Bawcock's Eve as well as the Wassails.

Bodmin Wassail

'Each year on 6th January (or the 5th, if the 6th falls on a Sunday), a group of men make their way around the Cornish town of Bodmin, singing wassail songs to the locals. They dress in top hat and tails, smart outfits comprised of "gentlemen's hand-me-downs" – clothes acquired from the local gentry and passed down from one wassailer to another over the decades.' (Bodmin Wassail website).

Although it has a known, unbroken tradition of nearly four hundred years, the Bodmin Wassail is strangely missing from so many accounts of British wassailing. We were, therefore, a little apprehensive driving up to meet Paul Scoble and the other wassailers: did they consider their event private and were they, in fact, reluctant or perhaps even regretting their decision to meet us? Not a bit of it! We arrived at Paul's house in the late afternoon to a warm welcome by his wife and family, who gave us tea and cake while we awaited the arrival of the wassailers who had been out since midday, wassailing around the houses. When they arrived, they stood at the front door and sang the first wassail song, then came in for refreshments, some chat and more singing. When the time came to leave, and after the old wassail song, we went with them to meet Jenny who had kindly invited us to join the amazing wassail feast at her house – the table was laden with home-made food.

Jenny told us that the wassailers had been coming to her house for ten or twelve years and, since her husband Harold died, they pile their hats on the chair he used to sit in. She added, *'Then they'll have a drink and toast Harold. Sometimes the hats fall down so we say, "Look Harold, behave yourself!"'*

While we will never know when this tradition began in Bodmin, we do know that in 1624 Nicholas Sprey, who had three times been Mayor, as well as Town Clerk, and MP for Bodmin, died and bequeathed in his will the sum of 13s 4d (approximately 66p in today's money) for an 'annual wassail cup' to promote 'the continuance of love and

Harold's Chair at Jenny's house, where the Wassailers pile their hats in his memory

neighbourly meetings' and 'remember all others to carry a more charitable conscience'. The wassail cup was to be taken to the Mayor's house each year on the twelfth day of Christmas, raising funds as it passed through the town. Although this stipend was withdrawn in 1838 the custom continues.

The wassailing day starts with a visit to the Mayor and local councillors at the Bodmin Town Council offices. After singing here they move on to sing in people's homes, local businesses, pubs, and residential homes, announcing their arrival by singing a wassail. After a full day and evening's wassailing they end up in the Masons Arms, with more singing and more collecting money for charity.

Tom Green Sr, Bodmin Wassailer for over 70 years until the late 1980s, recalled how the wassail bowl disappeared sometime during the Second World War. Unlike many wassail bowls which are made of wood and decorated with greenery, Bodmin's bowl was made of pottery. In 2008 former Mayor John Chapman, presented the Bodmin wassailers with a specially commissioned bowl, made by Lostwithiel potter John Webb. This is displayed throughout the year in the Tourist Information Centre in Bodmin's Shire Hall.

For many years the money collected for local charities was put in an old plastic ice-cream box with a hole cut in the lid; however wassailer Paul Scoble's father has now donated a new collecting box based on one used for decades by the bell ringers of St Petroc's Church, Bodmin. A new leather purse has also been donated, inspired by lyrics in one of the Bodmin Wassail songs:

'We've got a little purse made of stretching leather skin.
We want a little of your money, to bind it well within'.

According to the Bodmin Wassailers' website, the songs are the most important element of the wassail, and Bodmin has three. This is unusual, perhaps unique. Generally there is just one associated with a particular place. Bodmin's First Wassail song, is sung as the wassailers arrive and before entering the house. There is a certain fluidity in the actual verses sung on any given occasion – they may be sung in any order, or some even missed out.

The second wassail song is often one of the songs sung during a visit, while the eating, drinking, storytelling and fundraising goes on. This wassail song was passed on by Charlie Wilson, one of the wassailers for about 20 years, who had learnt it when in St Columb Boys' Home in about 1910, and he thought it may originally have been the St Columb Wassail. Charlie passed this song on in 1980, just two years before he died.

As the wassailers leave they sing the third song, the Old Wassail, sometimes complete, sometimes just the last verse and chorus. According to the late wassailer Tom Green Sr, this song has been sung since at least the late nineteenth century. A printed copy of this was given to wassailer Vic Legg in the mid 1970s by his colleague Vic Barratt, whose father, Vic Barratt Sr, had been a wassailer in the 1940s.

During the day's visits many songs are sung alongside the wassails, including well known Cornish favourites such as 'Camborne Hill', 'White Rose' and 'Little Eyes', each wassailer seemed to have his own party piece and we heard wonderful renditions of 'Tavistock Goosey Fair', and even Country classic, Roger Miller's 'King of the Road'! This singing, like so much traditional Cornish singing, is most definitely inclusive: *'It isn't a show; it's for people to join in with.'* (Vic Legg.)

Vic Legg, who has acquired a vast knowledge of local traditions, told us about

Mayor pouring drink for the Wassailers, 1953

another rediscovered song: *'We called on a family in Rhind Street several years ago, and there was a lady said, "what about this song, then:*

> *We are a couple of the Rhind Street boys,*
> *We are a couple of the boys,*
> *We knows our manners,*
> *We spends our tanners,*
> *We are welcome wherever we go!*
> *When we're going up the old Fore Street,*
> *Doors and windows open wide,*
> *You can hear the people say,*
> *Put those tuppenny Woodbines away,*
> *We are the Rhind Street boys!*
> *The Rhind Street boys went over the top, parley voo,*
> *The Rhind Street boys went over the top, parley voo,*
> *The Rhind Street boys went over the top,*
> *The Kaiser said he'd shoot the lot, Inky pinky parley voo!"*

We don't want to lose that! It hasn't been sung so far tonight, but it might be later on, out in the houses.'

There are currently ten wassailers who are all, quite rightly, proud of their tradition, each one having been invited to join by an existing wassailer. Vic Legg describes his initiation into wassailing thus: *'In 1974, I was asked if I'd like to go around and see what it's like, you've got to go as a coat-boy, you can't go straight in! They gotta approve of you, and you gotta approve of them. We weren't even allowed in anybody's house! We had to stand outside, wait for them to come out!'*

In the article by John Stephens referred to earlier in our introduction to the Wassail

Bodmin Wassail bowl made by John Webb in 2008

chapter, 'Cornish wassailing' in the Old Cornwall Society journal of 1932, Sir Arthur Quiller-Couch, the well-known literary figure, relates his personal reflections on the wassailing in Bodmin and Fowey, and also of his father from the earlier part of the nineteenth century. Quiller-Couch's father wrote down the words of the wassail song he heard and Stephens published them too in his article. This version has eleven verses, while by 2016 there were only six similar but not identical verses. Among the verses not sung when we visited is the following:

'The roads are so dirty, our shoes are got thin
But we have a bowl-dish to put money in.
For singing wassail, wassail,
And joy come to our jolly wassail.

Sometimes it is laurel, sometimes it is bay
Come fill up our bowl-dish and we'll drink away
For singing wassail, wassail,
And joy come to our jolly wassail'.

In the current 'First Wassail', the word 'Johnny' in the chorus replaces 'joy' (as in the above), but the Bodmin Wassailers say that that is how they inherited it, so this is how they will sing it. One of the present day verses is unusual as it refers to the sea. Stephens included this verse saying that it was given to him by Quiller-Couch, and that it was sung by St Austell singers when visiting Fowey. Paul Scoble aptly described tradition as *'a rolling thing'*.

Bodmin Wassail
As sung by the Bodmin Wassailers 6th January 2016

The First Song: (on arrival)
Chorus:
For singing wassail, wassail, wassail,
And Johnny come to our jolly wassail

Here comes the ship out in full sail –
Ploughs the wide ocean in many a gale.

We wish you a merry Christmas and a happy New Year
Pockets of money and a cellar of beer

If you've got an apple I hope you've got ten
To make some sweet cider 'gainst we comes again

Come knock at the knocker and ring at the bell
I know you'll reward us for singing wassail

If master and missus are sitting at ease
Put your hands in your pockets and give what you please.

The Old Song (when leaving)
Chorus:
Wassail, Wassail, Wassail Wassail
I am joy come to our jolly wassail

This is our merry night for choosing King and Queen
Then be it your delight that something maybe seen (to have some jam and splits!)
In our Wassail

Is there any butler here or dweller in this house
I hope they'll take a full carouse and enter to our bowl
In our Wassail

Our wassail bowl to fill with apples and good spice
Now grant us your goodwill to taste here once or twice
Of our Wassail

We fellows are all poor can't buy no house nor land
Unless we do gain in our Wassail

So now we must be gone to seek for more good cheer
Where bounty will be shown as we have found it here
In our Wassail

Bodmin Wassail First Song TRADITIONAL

CD 2 Track 12

Bodmin Wassail Old Song TRADITIONAL

Cotehele Wassail

The week before Christmas in 2016 we went to Cotehele in East Cornwall, a beautiful old Tudor Manor House now owned by the National Trust, on the banks above the Tamar, to experience the Cotehele Wassail.

It was great fun following the procession of the 'Oss, musicians and many families with all kinds of shakers, tambourines, hooters and even pots and pans. Mike James, was the Green Man, who normally plays the tea chest bass as a member of the Calstock Rubber Band. They made up the core of the musicians there. When we arrived at the Old Orchard the blessing of the apple trees began and everyone clattered, tooted and banged their instruments to ward off the evil spirits. We then wound round the garden paths to the New Orchard where the same thing happened. One of the things we really liked was that everyone, young and old, could join in with whatever they had to hand to make a noise – they didn't have to be able to play or sing anything and the atmosphere when everyone was hollering or banging something together was delightful.

'That's part of it; you've got to make lots of noise. It's inclusive,' Rosie Fierek said to us afterwards. She is a founder member of the Calstock Rubber Band and was also part of the Tamar Troylers a band that Marion and Patrick Coleman, Hilary's parents, created with Rosie and her husband Rob in the 1980s. She wrote the Wassail:

Rosie Fierek, musician and composer of Cotehele Wassail, 2016

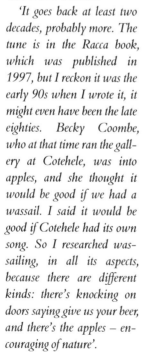

'It goes back at least two decades, probably more. The tune is in the Racca book, which was published in 1997, but I reckon it was the early 90s when I wrote it, it might even have been the late eighties. Becky Coombe, who at that time ran the gallery at Cotehele, was into apples, and she thought it would be good if we had a wassail. I said it would be good if Cotehele had its own song. So I researched wassailing, in all its aspects, because there are different kinds: there's knocking on doors saying give us your beer, and there's the apples – encouraging of nature'.

Rosie didn't find any

The Gurt Oss at Cotehele old orchard, 2016

specific background to wassails in East Cornwall but due to the Tamar Valley being famed for its market gardens and fruit growing a wassail that blesses the apples seemed entirely appropriate. She knew the Redruth Wassail and the Gloucester Wassail and amalgamated strands from several parts of the tradition, including the lilting 3/4 timing of many of the tunes.

'Then all we did – there were four members of the Tamar Troylers: two Colemans and two Fiereks, and a couple of staff from the estate, and we'd come here and do it, pouring cider on the trees and hanging toast in the branches, to encourage Robin. It started to grow, people latched on to it. There was a lull for a couple of years, and then it was revived. They decided to make it bigger; Cotehele took it on and advertised it. The event grew and grew and we have, on occasion, had several hundred in attendance. The song has been used from the earliest days of what now is a thriving tradition. The Calstock 'Oss is woken up each year to participate too'.

The 'Oss came from the tradition that was revived in Calstock in the 1970s and 80s of guising. The 'Oss used to dance round the streets of Calstock, to the tune 'Liskeard Fair', known then as the Gurt 'Oss after the only working horse in Calstock, which used to pull trucks along the tramlines on the quay to take ore and other materials. *'Once the loaded wagons reached the quayside they were towed away to their correct destination by a large horse kept specifically for this purpose. In its heyday the quayside must have had several of these, but the one living on in the memory of the older people was always called the "gurt 'oss". In fact no steam driven engine ever graced the quays of Calstock'.* (P. Coleman)

The 'Oss effigy was made by Hilary's brother. Part of its 'skirt' was from her mother's Scottish dancing dress and Hilary was delighted to see that the costume was still intact! For the procession they continued the tradition of playing Liskeard Fair and they also sometimes add Saltash. Rosie feels it important that people know that they are local tunes.

'I also like the fact that at Cotehele, we take the luck of the old Mother Orchard to the New Orchard. The song is sung at the oldest tree and at the youngest tree, we've always done that. The important part of tradition is that it is living. That it evolves through time. That people take owner-ship of it'.

This idea of tradition evolving is illustrated by the fact that in Saltash a revival of an old tradition has started, Kalan Gwav (first day of winter) or Allantide. This is an old Cornish festival that was traditionally celebrated on the night of 31 October, as well as the following day time on the 1st of November. Apples have a strong association with the festival so it seemed natural that Rosie was asked by Hilary Frank, the mayor of Saltash, who liked the Cotehele Wassail event, to create a song: the Essa Wassail. Essa is the old name for Saltash.

'There aren't any orchards yet in the town but, the song is all about "promise of things to come". It is already propagating as a couple of choirs have requested that they can use it; and the mayor has ambitions for all the local schools to sing it next year'. (R. Fierek)

Cotehele Wassail
As sung at Cotehele Orchards, St Dominic, December 2016

1. Come all ye keen wassailers treading the dirt
Lace up your boots and tighten your shirt
Our path it is clear and our purpose is plain
Let the new orchards blossom again and again

Chorus
Here's a toast to the apples and fruit of the wood
Good luck in the New Year; tread firm in the mud!

2. Let's scatter the ash to promote the new growth
And stir Mother Nature from her winter's sloth
We'll make lots of noise and dip cider with bread
To drive away Nick – welcome Robin instead

3. Give us your cider and give us your beer
We'll give you good music and fill up your ear
Tramping the path here we go, merry few
Carrying good luck from the old to the new

Cotehele Wassail ROSIE FIEREK (circa. 1993)

CD 2 Track 13

Come all ye keen was-sail-ers tread-ing the dirt, (Oh) lace up your boots and

tight-en your shirt. Our path, it is clear, and our pur-pose is plain. Let the

new or-chards blos-som a-gain and a-gain. Here's a toast to the ap-ples and

fruit of the wood. Good luck in the New Year, tread firm in the mud!

Redruth Wassail

Our first outing to record the carols around Cornwall in November 2015 was aptly enough in Redruth for the revival of the Redruth Wassail. We had a brilliant time singing under the town clock where the wassail bowl was presented to the Mayor of Redruth, before taking it from pub to pub with a whole host of musicians and singers, and the goodwill of the pubs was evident too, finishing at the Miner's Arms. Here's to many more!

The revival was partly organised by the Cornish Culture Association led by Simon Reed who says: *'For the first time in a generation the Redruth Wassail returned to the town in 2015. The Cornubian Oddfellows in Redruth are the custodians of the bowl on behalf of the Cornish Culture Association which remains in their hall. The bowl was commissioned and decorated by local artist Pol Jenkin. The custom is now set to occur on the last Saturday of November every year'. He adds: 'It was the custom in Redruth to visit properties as the Wassailers saw fit. The household would then reward the singers with a drink or some other form of refreshment, saffron cake was a popular choice. Traditional Cornish drinks like "Shenagrum"* (Dark beer, brown sugar and lemon served hot) *and "Mahogany"* (Gin and black treacle) *were popular rewards.'* (Simon Reed 2015)

Redruth Wassail bowl made by Pol Jenkin

Two men were responsible for the collection of Cornish folk carols around Camborne and Redruth in the beginning of the twentieth century. Jim Thomas and Tom Miners were prolific recorders of folk traditions and active members of the Old Cornwall Society movement in the 1920s. 'Jim Thomas had also been Cecil Sharp's contact when he visited Cornwall in 1913 and 1914 providing him with some material direct and also introducing him to singers'. (Merv Davey, An Daras, Cornish Folk Tradition website) And so this wassail song was recorded by Cecil Sharp in 1913 from the singing of John Trenerry of Redruth and published in the *Journal of the Folk-Song Society* in 1914. It was written as 'warzail' in the verses because of the accent. Sharp goes on to say:

> 'The ancient custom of wassailing still lingers in Redruth and the neighbourhood. Mr Trenerry told me that in his younger days small parties of five or six men would go out wassailing between Christmas and the New Year. They carried a wooden bowl, seven to nine inches in diameter, with sprigs of holly and ivy fixed vertically round the edge.'

In a later *Journal of the Folk-Song Society*, 1929, four very similar versions were printed and had been collected by Thomas and Miners but there are some interesting variations. One, from Mrs Woolcock, Park Road, Camborne, in 1926 is only a fragment and uses the word 'Moorzeal' instead of wassail. 'Moorzeal' was also used in a version from a Penponds singer which included 'snatches of the St George play':

> "In come I, little man Jack
> With my wife upon my back
> Moorzeal etc
> In comes I old Beelzebub,
> On my shoulder I carry a club
> Moorzeal etc."

The Cornish St George plays, of which several versions have been taken down in West Cornwall, usually end with some verses of the wassail song, which accounts for the above version, although the words are difficult to fit to the tune.' (J. Thomas)

Merv Davey says: *'Wassail singing was at one time widespread throughout Cornwall and embedded in the Christmas Guising traditions'*. Thomas continues: 'If householders were unwilling to give to the Wassail Boys the blessings would be turned to curses and insults as in the verse:

> "The Mistress and master they won't give a fig
> But set down by the fire and grunt like a pig
> A-wersey, A-wersey
> Joy come home with Johnny Wersey"

This corruption has given rise to a personification.'

Also in the journal is 'Here Come We A-Wassailing' sung by Mr W J Bennetts, aged

72, Tolcarne Street, Camborne, in 1926. The tune is a variant of the one found in Bramley and Stainer's *Christmas Carols New and Old* (1878), but the words of the first verse have been altered from 'Leaves so green' to 'Lucy Green':

> 'Here come we a-wassailing 'long with our Lucy Green
> And here we come a-wand'ring as fair as to be seen.'

Jim Thomas observes that it has 'given rise to an interesting custom. The Camborne Carol Party of which Mr Bennetts was a member, used to carry with them a small child dressed in evergreens, their "Lucy Green". This is evidently a substitute for the older wassail bowl. Another carol choir in the district was known as the "Turkey Claw Choir", the collector carrying a turkey's claw in virtue of his office. Mr Miners thinks this might be a relic of the insignia of the old "privileged choirs".' (J. Thomas)

The use of the term 'privileged choirs' is intriguing and we'd love to know more.

The Redruth Wassail
As sung at Redruth November 2015

1. The Mistress and Master our wassail begin,
Pray open the door and let us come in.

Chorus: With our wassail, wassail, wassail, wassail;
And joy come to our jolly wassail

2. The Mistress and Master sitting down by the fire,
While we poor wassailers are travelling in mire.

3. The Mistress and Master sitting down at their ease,
Put their hands in their pockets and give what they please.

4. I hope that your apple trees will prosper and bear,
That we may have cyder when we call next year.

5. And where you've one hogshead I hope you'll have ten.
So we may have cyder when we call again.

6. I hope that your barley will prosper and grow,
That you may have some and enough to bestow.

7. Now we poor wassail boys growing weary and cold,
Drop a small bit of silver into our bowl.

8. I wish you a blessing and a long time to live,
Since you've been so free and so willing to give.

Redruth Wassail TRADITIONAL arr. Ian Marshall
CD 2 Track 14

1.The Mis-tress and Mas-ter our was-sail be - gin pray o - pen your door_ and

1.The Mis-tress and Mas-ter our was-sail be - gin pray o - pen your door_ and

1.The Mis-tress and Mas-ter our was-sail be - gin pray o - pen your door and

Chorus

let us come in_ With our_ was - sail was-sail was - sail_ was-

let us come in_ With our_ was - sail was - sail was - sail_ was-

let us come in_ With our_ was - sail was - sail was - sail was-

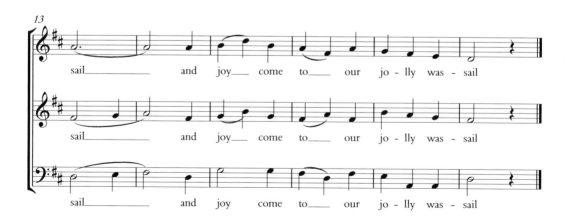

sail_ and joy_ come to_ our jo - lly was - sail

sail_ and joy_ come to_ our jo - lly was - sail

sail_ and joy come to_ our jo - lly was - sail

Tom Bawcock

'A merry place you may believe, was Mouzel 'pon Tom Bawcock's Eve!'

So says the first line of the chorus of this song, and indeed it was a very merry place when we visited on 23 December 2015. We had two carol visits to make this evening, the first had us parking at Paul and walking down the hill into Mousehole feeling the festive atmosphere grow as more and more people joined us with children and lanterns. We stood on the harbourside, meeting friends and enjoying the lights around the harbour waiting for the procession to come through. Until the early 1990s the celebrations were very much centred around the pubs, but now each year the teachers, children and parents from Mousehole School make withy lanterns of fishes which they carry through the streets from the school to the harbourside where they meet Tom Bawcock (pronounced 'bow' to rhyme with 'low'), in his 'boat on bracers', a withy boat on shoulder-braces.

As we watched the procession reach the slipway they stopped, to sing and to send small lantern-boats out onto the sea. This was when we took the opportunity to record Mousehole Male Voice Choir and others singing 'Tom Bawcock', before we walked back up the hill to Paul.

Brenda Wooton's daughter, Sue Ellery-Hill, in her book *Pantomime Stew*, tells us of her memories of Tom Bawcocks Eve. Upon realising they would never get a seat anywhere in Mousehole they: 'would all traipse up to the Engine Inn at Nancledra to join

Starry Gazey pie lights, Mousehole, 2016

in with the crowds singing the old Cornish Carols.' So, we were in good company seeking Cornish carols in a nearby pub as we headed into Penzance and the Dock Inn, for further celebrations, where we had our second visit of the evening and recorded 'Go Your Way Green Leaves' and the Pendeen version of 'While Shepherds Watched'.

Back in Mousehole, this festival is held every year on 23 December and is a celebration of Tom Bawcock, who is said to have been the only fisherman brave enough to go out in the prolonged and severe weather conditions which had led to starvation in Mousehole. He brought back a good catch of fish, famously including seven varieties, which was shared amongst the people of Mousehole, and was made into a number of dishes including the now-famous Starry Gazey Pie. This fish pie is traditionally made with fish, egg and potatoes in the filling and a pastry lid, with the heads and tails of fish poking through and gazing at the stars. If you are lucky enough to be in Mousehole on Tom Bawcock's Eve, you can, in return for a donation to the RNLI, try the pie at the Ship Inn. The story of Tom Bawcock has been made more nationally famous with the publication of Antonia Barber's book for children, *The Mousehole Cat*, in 1991, and its subsequent 1994 BBC television production. In 1999, Bawcock's Eve, a radio play set in Mousehole, and written by the well-known Cornish playwright Nick Darke, was first aired on BBC Radio 4. Cornish singer Brenda Wootton included the song on four of her albums: *Piper's Folk* (1968), *Starry Gazey Pie* (1975), *Way Down to Lamorna* (1984) and *Voice of Cornwall* (1996).

Although the origins are unknown, the first recorded description of these celebrations as they were around the end of the nineteenth century, was made by Robert Morton Nance in the *Journal of the Old Cornwall Society* in 1927. He described it as 'a feast among the fisher-folk, its particular feature was the eating at it of seven different sorts of fish, salt or fresh, scrowled or marinated, boiled, grilled, or fried, with, accord-

Robert Morton Nance (1873-1959), authority on Conish language and joint founder of the Old Cornwall Society

ing to the custom of the old smuggling days, plenty of "moonshine" to wash them down'. As Morton Nance says: 'here is a little verse about it, written years ago, that I have turned out of a drawer'. Ralph Dunstan subsequently set the words to an old Cornish dance tune called the 'Wedding March' also in the 1920s.

Mousehole is now justifiably famous for its Christmas lights, as well as for its Tom Bawcock's celebrations. In 1963, Joan Gillchrest, an artist based in Mousehole, suggested brightening up the harbourside with strings of coloured bulbs along both quays. Since then, the lights have become much more elaborate and include many designs and set pieces based around Christmas and the sea. The lights are lit each evening from the middle of December until 6 January. However they are dimmed between 8-9pm on 19 December every year in memory of those who gave their lives in the Penlee Lifeboat disaster of December 1981. The RNLI lifeboat, *Solomon Browne*, was launched that evening from the Penlee Lifeboat Station in Newlyn, into huge seas to go to the aid of the MV Union Star, which was in trouble off the Cornish coast. A Royal Naval Sea King helicopter was also scrambled to help in the rescue attempt, but despite truly heroic efforts the lifeboat and all eight crew members were lost, along with the five crew and three family members, of the Union Star. Lt Cdr Smith, US Navy, the Sea King pilot, later reported that: 'The greatest act of courage that I have ever seen, and am ever likely to see, was the penultimate courage and dedication shown by the Penlee crew when it manoeuvred back alongside the casualty in over 60 ft breakers and rescued four people shortly after the Penlee lifeboat had been bashed on top of the casualty's hatch covers. They were truly the bravest eight men I've ever seen, who were also totally dedicated to upholding the highest standards of the RNLI'. At the funeral of these men, Mousehole Male Voice Choir sang 'Sunset and Evening Star'.

Tom Bawcock
As sung by Mousehole Male Voice Choir and others at Tom Bawcock's Eve, Mousehole, December 2015

Chorus:
A merry plaace you may believe
Was Mouzel 'pon Tom Bawcock's eve.
To be there then who wudn' wesh
To sup o' sibm soorts o' fesh!

1. When morgy brath had cleared the path
Comed lances for a fry
An' then us had a bit o' scad
An' starry gazey pie!

2. Next comed fairmaids bra' thusty jaades
As maade our oozles dry
An' ling and haake enough to maake
A raunin' shark to sigh!

3. As aich we'd clunk as health were drunk
In bumpers bremmen high
An' when up caame Tom Bawcock's naame
We praised 'un to the sky!

(*Mouzel* = Mousehole, *Morgy brath* = Dogfish broth, *Lances* = Sand Eels,
Scad = Horse Mackerel, *Fairmaids* = Pilchards, *Oozles* = Throats, *Clunk* = Swallow)

Tom Bawcock Tune: **CORNISH WEDDING MARCH, words: R. MORTON NANCE arr. S. Lawry**

CD 2 Track 15

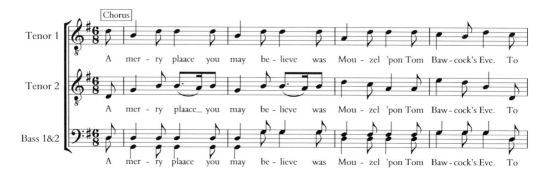

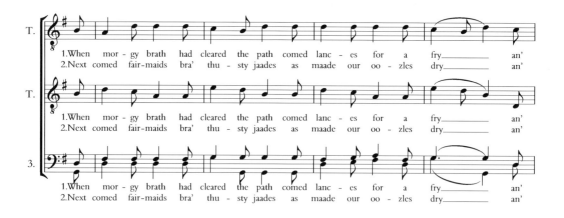

Wassail the Silver Apple

One of our earlier visits was, uncharacteristically, not just in daylight, but also in sunshine! We travelled one morning to the Kitchen Café in Tremenheere Sculpture Park near Penzance, where Pip Wright practices one of her singing groups, Dawn Chorus. They had invited us down to hear them sing 'Wassail the Silver Apple', written just a few years ago by Mike O'Connor, and now one of their favourite winter songs. On this occasion Dawn Chorus had been joined by members of another of Pip's choirs, Levow an Bys (World Voices in Cornish), bringing the total number of singers up to about sixty. The cafe is a lovely venue, light and airy, with great acoustics and a wonderful view down to St Michael's Mount. After their practice we stayed on, enjoying the sunshine and the view, for a natter with friends and some coffee and cake!

Pip Wright is passionate about music, particularly harmony singing; she says singing *'is a way to connect with ourselves and each other, to build community, to let what's inside out and for our general well-being. I enjoy working with non-auditioned groups and especially with people who may have missed out on music in the past, to help them find their voice and gain an understanding of how music works through musicianship'*. Pip not only leads the singing groups Dawn Chorus and Levow an Bys, but works with other groups that use singing therapeutically, such as the first Singing for the Brain group in Cornwall, for people with dementia and their carers, and Breathing Space, the first group in Cornwall to use singing to help those who live with chronic lung health conditions.

This modern wassail song, also known as the 'Kit Hill Wassail', was written in 1999 for wassailing the orchard of John Heslop and Kathy Wallis who then lived on the slopes of Kit Hill, at Kelly Bray. In this wassail Mike O'Connor's words refer to the superstitions that lie behind orchard wassails: *'I tried to take both singers and listeners a little*

Above: Dawn Chorus at Tremenheere, 2015

Right: Mike O'Connor, musicologist, expert on the history of Cornish music

closer to the medieval world in which the tradition evolved'. Later, Kathy moved to Rillaton, starting up an annual wassail there for her apple trees, and Mike wrote the 'Rillaton Wassail' for them. Both these wassails are published by Lyngham House Music and are both sung at the wassail in Rillaton.

The version sung by Dawn Chorus includes a Cornish introduction which was translated by Jim Daniel and Pol Hodge, and harmonies as arranged by Sarah Morgan.

Composer Mike O'Connor lived in Wales, London and Scotland before he moved to North Cornwall in the 1970s and has a strong connection with Padstow. He is well known as a fiddle and concertina player, and also as a storyteller, writing a book of Cornish folk tales. Mike has also done a lot of work in the field of historical musical research in Cornwall, and has published a book on his findings called *Ilow Kernow*. He was made a bard of the Cornish Gorsedd in 2002 when he took the bardic name Crowder, which means Fiddle Player. He is a well known songwriter and has produced and directed the folk operas *The Cry of Tin*, *Unsung Heroes* and *Cornish Lads*, which were part of the Cornwall Songwriters project. More recently he has been involved as musical consultant for the BBC series Poldark and has also written some of the songs and music.

Wassail the Silver Apple
As sung by Dawn Chorus at the Kitchen Café, Tremenheere Sculpture Park, Penzance December 2015

Chorus/Intro:
Bydh yagh! Bydh yagh! Re bo bledhen'tos,
Kres ha plenteth dhywgh hwi oll a vynno dos

Wassail! Wassail! May the coming year,
Peace and plenty bring, to all who wassail here.

Drink to the bud and the blossom.
Drink to the root of the tree.
Drink to the fruit of the summer.
Wassail! Let the cider run free!

Fire at the spirit of winter.
Fire at the spirit of night,
Fire at the spirit of darkness.
Wassail! The bringer of light!

Wassail the silver shilling.
Wassail the silver moon,
Wassail the silver apple.
Drink! Hail the sign of the sun!

Wassail the Silver Apple, M. J. O'CONNOR (1999), arr. Sarah Morgan,
Cornish translation of chorus Jim Daniel & Pol Hodge
CD 2 Track 16

Coda

'Anyone who has walked on a frosty starlit night through a Cornish village with local band and chapel choir will know that a Cornish Christmas means carol singing. Whether circled in the village square, or packed in the chapel, what singing it is! Strong and lively, merry and exuberant, resounding far through the clear air'. (Rev Ian Haile, sleeve notes to *Cornish Christmas*)

Christmas Bells

'Sing we for pleasure – for one and all' is the motto of the Four Lanes Male Choir.

It seems suitable to finish our book with a carol recorded on Christmas Day itself! In the morning Hilary went to Four Lanes to record the Choir in the square. There was a good turnout of people to listen to them and it's great that this tradition still endures.

The crowd in Four Lanes Square, Christmas morning, 2015

*Four Lanes
Male Voice
Choir
singing in
the square;
2015*

They sang several Merritt carols, amongst others, and finished with 'Christmas Bells', which was composed by one of their singers, Ronald Brown. Mr Brown was their Musical Director for thirty five years, having taken over the role from his uncle, Wilfrid Brown, who was Four Lanes Male Choir's first Musical Director. The choir was formed in 1944 to welcome home troops from the D-Day landings, and has gone on to become one of Cornwall's best known Male Voice Choirs. Today, under the leadership of Tim Hoskin, they continue their singing, rehearsing weekly in Four Lanes United Methodist Chapel.

Four Lanes is just five miles from Illogan, home of the great Cornish carol composer Thomas Merritt, so not surprisingly, they include all twelve of Thomas Merritt's carols in their repertoire. The choir have a long history of involvement with Cornish Carols and in 1982 featured on an album called *Carols of Cornwall* which was recorded at Truro Cathedral for a 'festival of carols with people thronging just everywhere' (from Carols of Cornwall sleeve notes). For many years the choir, along with Camborne Ladies Choir, has graced Camborne Wesley and Redruth Methodist Chapels each December with a concert of Merritt's carols. However, just weeks before the concert in 2016, which we had hoped to attend, Redruth's iconic Methodist Chapel closed down, leaving Camborne to carry on this tradition alone. In 2008, Four Lanes Male Choir, together with Mabe Ladies Choir, Camborne Circuit Ladies Choir and Redruth Methodist Church Choir recorded a CD at Redruth Methodist Chapel to celebrate Thomas Merritt's 200th anniversary. This CD, *A Cornish Christmas with Merritt*, has all twelve carols and his 'Coronation March' as an organ solo. A month after its release, eight hundred and fifty copies had been sold and sent around the world: 'Frank Curnow, chairman of Four Lanes Choir, said: "We ordered 500 in the first instance and then another 350, but all have gone. We have been inundated with orders. We know copies have been sent to the United States, Australia and the Falklands. They have gone wherever Cornish people have emigrated over the years.'" (*West Briton*). Because we were not able to record at Redruth Wesley Chapel, we were thankfully able to use as our first track 'Hark the Glad Sound' from this album.

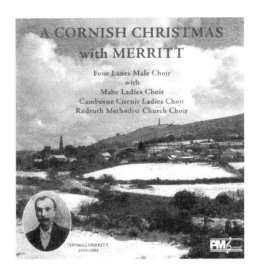

The organ that Thomas Merritt played when he was organist at the Chili Road Methodist Chapel at Illogan Highway is now in St Andrews Church at Pencoys, Four Lanes. Chili Road Chapel closed in 1973 and has since been demolished. £3,500 was raised for a major restoration of the organ (which was built by Hele of Plymouth) in 2001, including £932 donated by members of the California Cornish Cousins, showing how well Merritt is thought of in the Cornish Diaspora.

We were lucky to meet Malcolm, the son of Wilfrid Brown, at a concert in Four Lanes, where he told us that it was his father who had begun the tradition of carolling in Four Lanes, going from house to house. Nowadays the carolling is only outside the Victoria Inn in the square. Malcolm was also the church organist at Redruth Methodist Church for over five decades from 1963, playing there every week. *As a boy in 1947, I went to my church where I was brought up in Four Lanes and the organist hadn't turned up. I had only had three or four lessons, but I was asked to play for the service, so I did'*. (Malcolm Brown)

'Of all the Cornish carols none are sung with more enthusiasm or rapture than those of Thomas Merritt. The four Cornish Choirs on this CD capture the feeling of joy and wonder that only these pieces can engender' (Sleeve notes, *A Cornish Christmas with Merritt*, 2008)

Christmas Bells
As sung by the Four Lanes Male Voice Choir at Four Lanes Square, Christmas morning, 2015

The Christmas bells are ringing,
What message are they bringing?
Ding-Dong, Ding-Dong, Ding-Dong,
Merry Christmas everyone!

The children carol singing,
The sleighbells too are ringing
Ting-a-ling, Ting-a-ling, Ting-a-ling,
Merry Christmas everyone!

Christmas Bells R. BROWN
CD 2 Track 17

Appendices

A: Places visited

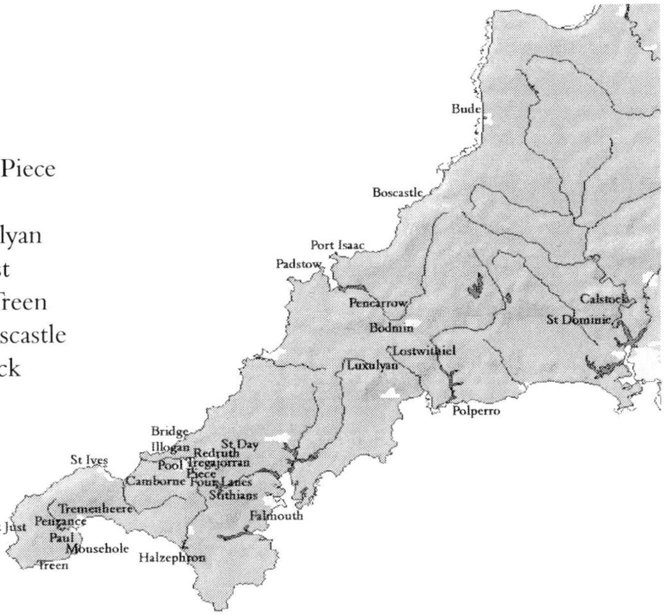

Pubs
Halzephron Inn
The Countryman Inn, Piece
The Dock, Penzance
The Kings Arms, Luxulyan
The Kings Arms, St Just
The Logan Rock Inn, Treen
The Napoleon Inn, Boscastle
The Tamar Inn, Calstock

Concerts & Services
Bridge Chapel, nr.
    Portreath
Fore Street
    Methodist
    Chapel, St Ives
Heartlands, Pool
Paul Church
Paynters Lane End Chapel, Illogan
Pencarrow House
Stithians Village Hall
The Parkhouse Centre, Bude

Outdoors
Bodmin Town
Camborne Square
Cotehele Gardens, St Dominic
Falmouth Town
Four Lanes Square

Mousehole Harbour
Padstow Town
Redruth Town
St Day Square
Tregajorran Square

Rehearsals
North Street, Lostwithiel
Polperro Methodist Chapel
The Temperance Hall, Port Isaac
Tremenheere Sculpture Gardens Cafe

B. Carols in order of frequency heard on our visits

Carol	Frequency	Where
Hark the Glad Sound (Merritt)	17	Countryman Inn, Dock Inn, Halzephron Inn, Kings Arms (Lux.), Kings Arms (St Just), The Logan Rock Inn, The Tamar Inn, Paul Church, Paynters Lane End Chapel, Stithians, Camborne, Falmouth, Four Lanes, Redruth, St Day, Tregajorran, Polperro Chapel
The Star of Bethlehem	14	Countryman Inn, Dock Inn, Halzephron, Inn, Kings Arms (Lux.), Kings Arms (St Just), The Logan Rock Inn, Bridge Chapel, Stithians, Camborne, Falmouth, Four Lanes, Padstow, Redruth, Polperro Chapel
While Shepherds Watched (Lyngham)	14	Countryman Inn, Dock Inn, Halzephron Inn, Kings Arms (Lux.), Kings Arms (St Just), The Logan Rock Inn, The Tamar Inn, Paynters Lane End Chapel, Camborne, Falmouth, Four Lanes, Redruth, St Day, Tregajorran
Hark What Music Fills Creation	9	Countryman Inn, Dock Inn, Halzephron, Inn, The Logan Rock Inn, Paul Church, St Ives Chapel, Camborne, Falmouth, Four Lanes
Hail Sacred Day, Auspicious Morn	8	Countryman Inn, Halzephron Inn, The Logan Rock Inn, Paynters Lane End Chapel, St Ives Chapel, Stithians, Camborne, Falmouth
St Day Carol	8	Countryman Inn, Dock Inn, Halzephron Inn, The Logan Rock Inn, The Tamar Inn, Bude, Redruth, St Day
The Holly and the Ivy	7	Countryman Inn, Halzephron Inn, The Logan Rock Inn, Bridge Chapel, Heartlands, Tregajorran, Lostwithiel
Seraphic Minstrels (Sound, Sound)	7	Countryman Inn, Dock Inn, Halzephron Inn, The Logan Rock Inn, Bridge Chapel, Falmouth, Tregajorran

Carol	Frequency	Where
Redruth Wassail	4	Countryman Inn, Bridge Chapel, Redruth, Tregajorran
Hellesveor	4	Countryman Inn, Dock Inn, Paul Church, St Ives Chapel
The Angels' Song (Glory Glory)	3	Countryman Inn, Kings Arms (Lux), Tregajorran
Boscastle Jack	3	Countryman Inn, Kings Arms (Lux), The Napoleon
Go Your Way Green Leaves	3	Countryman Inn, Dock Inn, Tregajorran
Tom Bawcock	3	Countryman Inn, Dock Inn, Mousehole
A Virgin Most Pure	2	Countryman Inn, Bridge Chapel
Sapphire Throne	2	Bridge Chapel, Camborne
While Shepherds Watched (Newlyn)	2	Paul Church, Pencarrow
While Shepherds Watched (Bolingey)	2	Countryman Inn, Bridge Chapel
Awake Ye Nations (Wakey, Wakey)	2	Countryman Inn, Tregajorran

The following carols were unique to their locality or event: Can Dilly (The Dilly Song) at Heartlands; Calm on the Listening Ear of Night at Pencarrow; Flaming Seraphs (The Stratton Carol) at Bude; Hark the Glad Sound (Port Isaac) at Port Isaac; Karol, Karol Kristyon at Bridge Chapel; Rouse, Rouse at Padstow; While Shepherds Watched (Pendeen) at The Dock Inn; While Shepherds Watched (Stithians) at Stithians; 'Tis Christmas Time at Polperro Chapel; Bodmin Wassail at Bodmin; Cotehele Wassail at Cotehele; Wassail the Silver Apple at Tremenheere; Christmas Bells at Four Lanes.

C. Timeline of collections containing Cornish carols

Late 1700s	Notebook four handwritten carols, possibly from Hayle area
1810-88	Tregony manuscripts
1823	*Some Ancient Christmas Carols*, Davies Gilbert
1825	Hutchens manuscripts, thirty nine carols
1833	*Christmas Carols, Ancient and Modern*, W. Sandys

1860	*A Collection of Ancient Christmas Carols*, Sedding, Bristol
1870	*A Selection of Carols, Pieces, and Anthems, a pocket book of words*, F. Rodda, Penzance
1870	*The Cornubian Tune Book*, R. Jones, Penzance
1875	*Carols for Use in Church*, R. R. Chope
1880s	Thomas Merritt's compositions, printed at his own expense
1889 & earlier?	*Christmas Carols, Pieces & Anthems a pocket book of words*, Doidge 'Steam printer', Redruth
1889	*Cornish Carols*, parts 1 & 2, R. H. Heath, Redruth
1893	*The Christmas Welcome*, J. H. Thomas, Moonta, Australia
1892	*Old Cornish Carols*, Joseph Leese, Redruth
1894	*A New Christmas Carol*, R. H. Heath, Redruth
1910	*Cornish Bells*, C. W. Stubbs, Truro
1911	*The Truro Carol Book*, Rev C. W. Stubbs
1912	*Old Christmas Carols and Anthems*, parts 1 & 2, Warmington, Carbis Bay
1920s?	*Christmas Carols Set to Music*, words only, Colan Williams
1920s?	*Six Christmas Carols*, parts 1 & 2, Merritt
1920s?	*A Collection of Cornish Carols*, J Davey, Adelaide, Australia
1923/5	*The Cornish Song Book*, R. Dunstan
1927	*Old Cornish Carols*, Tregony manuscripts, Barnicoat , Polperro
1929	*Twenty Six Celebrated Cornish Carols*, J Glasson, Kadina, Australia
1940s	*Six Old Carol Arrangements*, Maddern Williams
1957	*Sapphire Throne*, Donald Broad
1960-2000	*Four Christmas Carols*, S. Nicholas, reprinted three times from 'original blocks'
1960s	Heath's carols reprint, R. Vigo, Falmouth
1966	*Now Carol We*, twelve carols from Hutchens manuscripts, Inglis Gundry
1971	*Strike Sound, Padstow Carols*, Inglis Gundry
1977	*Twelve Cornish Carols*, T. Merritt, Lodenek Press
1982	*Carols of Cornwall*, K. Pelmear, Dyllansow Truran
1983	*Traces of Ancient Mystery*, R. McGrady
1984	*Cornish Carols in Australia*, P. Payton
2000?	*North Cornwall Carols*, T. Bale
2010	*Victorian Carols*, reprint of Heath's carols, Federation of Old Cornwall Society
2011	*Carols of the Stratton Hundred*, Michael Richardson, Bude & Stratton Old Cornwall Society
2017	*Hark! The Glad Sound of Cornish Carols*, H. Coleman & S. Burley, Redruth

D. Version of While Shepherds Watched known in Cornwall:
Either sung or talked about or in Cornish publications.

All Night, All Night, Charlie Jose, Roger Nicholls referred to this as the Tintagel version, also mentioned by Vic Legg

Angels' Song, *Cornubian Song Book*, R. Jones Penzance, 1870

Bolingey, W. Eade as What Melody, no 6 in Heath, *Cornish Carols;* known as Bolingey in Dunstan; Mount Zion in Polperro; St Day by Tereba Nessa Choir.

Boscastle Jack, Jack Davey, Boscastle with Sankey chorus, sung at the Napoleon Inn, Boscastle, 2016

Chiming Bells, John Bolitho referred to this as the Tintagel version, also sung at Polperro?

Kilkhampton, from Ivor Potter, *Carols of the Stratton Hundred*

Lyngham, T. Jarman, widely sung

New Tregoney, from W. C. Dunstone, Portloe in R. Dunstan

New, R. Dunstan: 'popular tune in many parts of Cornwall. It belongs to the Redruth-Camborne group'

Newlyn, arr. Maddern Williams, *Old Cornwall Tune*, still sung at various places including Paul, St Wenn, Boscastle

No 12, Leese, *Old Cornish Carols*, by Matthew Clemens 1892

No 4, Leese, *Old Cornish Carols*, 1892

No. 20, Heath, *Cornish Carols*, vol 1, Redruth, 1889

No. 30, Heath, *Cornish Carols*, vol 1, Redruth, 1889

No. 31, Heath, *Cornish Carols*, vol 1 by Niness [sic] (Helston), Redruth, 1889 & sung at Pencarrow House 2015

No. 9, Warmington vol 2

No.7, Warmington vol 1

Old St Gennys, from John Bolitho, *Carols of the Stratton Hundred*

Pendeen, arr. S. Lawry, Mousehole MVC still sung at various places including Penzance, Mousehole

Pendeen Miners' Choir, sung at the Dock Inn, 2015

Porthhallow, informed of by singers from St Keverne and Porthleven

Psalm Tune, Davies Gilbert, in minor key

St Gennys, Stephen Jose's MS, tune probably St. David's by James Taylor of Kintore, published in Aberdeen in 1820, sung at Pencarrow House

St Keverne, sung at Halzephron Inn, 2015

Stewart Biddick, remembers another Boscastle version according to R Nicholls

Stithians, written by L.H. Pascoe, Stithians, circa 1907

Stratton 1, alternative words to Mortals Awake, *Carols of the Stratton Hundred*

Stratton 2, both 1 & 2 from Ethel Jewell, *Carols of the Stratton Hundred*

'Tis Christmas Time, Polperro version

Treen, sung at the Dock and Logan Rock Inns 2015/6, recorded by P.Kennedy 1956

Trewolder, 'Glory Glory in the Highest', from Roger Nicholls, also Marhamchurch Anthem, *Carols of the Stratton Hundred*

Welshy, from the Lizard, informed of by singers from St Keverne and Porthleven

William Sandys, 'Traditional West Cornwall Carol melody'

Zadoc, Padstow or Old While Shepherds, 'Ould Zaddock' in R. Dunstan: 'I believe to be the oldest, it was formerly known from Padstow to Portloe and right down through West Cornwall. By about 1866 it had been discarded by many of the regular singers'

E: Bibliography, Discography & further sources

Songbooks

Arnold, J; *The Compleat Psalmodist*, Robert Brown, London, 1753

Bale, T., *North Cornwall Carols*, circa 2000

Baring-Gould, S., *Songs of the West*, Methuen, 1905

Barnicoat, B., *Old Cornish Carols*, Polperro Press, 1927

Bramley H. R. & Stainer J., *Christmas Carols New and Old*, Novello, Ewer & Co, London, 1878

Broad, D., *Hymn Tunes*, The Cornish Music Publication, 1964

Coleman H. & Burley S., *Shout Kernow*, Francis Boutle, 2015

Chope, R. R., *Carols for use in Church*, Metzler & Co and Novello, Ewer & Co, London, 1875

Davies Gilbert, *Some Ancient Christmas Carols*, John Nichols & Son, London, 1823

Dermer, P., Vaughan Williams R. & Shaw M., *The Oxford Book of Carols*, OUP, 1928

Dunstan, R., *Cornish Dialect & Folksongs*, Reid Bros, London, 1932

Dunstan, R., *Christmas Carols*, 1923

Dunstan R., *The Cornish Song Book, Lyver Canow Kernewek*, Reid Bros, London, 1928

Glasson, J., *Twenty Six Celebrated Cornish Carols*, 1927

Gundry, I., *Canow Kernow*, Dyllansow Truran, 1966

Gundry, I., *Strike Sound*, Lodenek Press, 1971

Gundry, I., *Now Carol We*, OUP, 1966

Heath R. H., *Cornish Carols*, parts 1 & 2, Heard & Sons, Redruth, 1889

Husk, *Songs of the Nativity*; J. C. Hotten, London, 1864

Keyte H. & Parrott A., *The New Oxford Book of Carols*, OUP, 1992

Leese J., *Old Cornish Carols*, Taylor, 1892

McGrady, R., *Traces of Ancient Mystery, The Ballad Carols of Davies Gilbert and William Sandys*, Institute of Cornish Studies, 1993

Merritt, T., *The Shepherd of Israel, Sacred Cantata*, Cowethas Ylow Kernewek, 1988

Merritt, T., *Twelve Cornish Carols*, Lodenek Press/Cornish Music Company, 1977

Nicholas, S., *Carols*, The Cornish Music Company, post 2000

O'Connor M., *Seasons, More Songs by Mike O'Connor*, Lyngham House, 1999

Payton, P., *Cornish Carols from Australia*, Truran, 1984

Pelmear, K., *Carols of Cornwall*, Dyllansow Truran, 1982

Richardson, M. J., *Carols of the Stratton Hundred North Cornwall*, Bude Stratton and District Old Cornwall Society, 2011

Sandys, W., *Christmas Carols, Ancient and Modern*, R. Beckley, London, 1833

Sankey, I., *Sacred Songs and Solos*. Morgan & Scott, London, 1890

Thomas J. H., *The Christmas Welcome, A Choice Collection of Cornish Carols*, Moonta, 1893

Thomas, W. H., *Cornish Songs and Ditties and other Rhymes*, Thomas, 1904

Townsend, J., *Cornish Carols By Candlelight*, 2015

Vigo, R., *Heath's Cornish Carols*, parts 1 &2 reprint, Welcome Publicity Ltd for Browser Books, Falmouth, circa 1960s

Warmington, T. N., *A Selection of Old Christmas Carols and Anthems*, parts I & II, Warmington, Carbis Bay, 1912

Williams, C., *Christmas Carols Set to Music*, St Ives, 1920s?

Other books

Barber, John T., *Cousin Jack Afloat and Ashore*, J. T. Barber, St Ives, 1969

Betjeman, J., *Sweet Songs of Zion*, Hodder & Stoughton, 2007

Biglow & Main, *Christmas Annual* No. 8, New York: Biglow & Main, 1877

Bottrell, W., *Traditions and Hearthside Stories of West Cornwall*, W.Cornish, Penzance 1870

Couch, J., *History of Polperro*, 1871

Green, R. & Langford, T., *Methodism in Stithians*, 1991

Gundry, I., *Last Boy of the Family: A Musical Memoir*, Thames, 1998

Hamilton Jenkin, A. K., *Cornish Homes and Customs*, J. M. Dent, 1934

Hardy, T., *Under the Greenwood Tree*, Tinsley Bros. London, 1872

Hunt, Robert, *Romances of the West of England*, J. C. Hotten, London,1865

James, C. C., *History of the Parish of Gwennap in Cornwall*; C. C. James, Cornwall, 1949

Julian J., *Dictionary of Hymnology*, Dover Publications, New York, 1907

McKinney, Gage, *When Miners Sang: the Grass Valley Carol Choir*, Comstock Bonanza Press, 2001

Molesworth-St Aubyn, H. H., *Notebook for the Register of Services, from St Petroc's Church*, Cornwall Records Library, 1858-61

Prior, O., *Cornish Pasty – A Book of Cartoons*; O. Prior, Adelaide, 1950

Pryce, William, *Archeologica Cornu-Britannica*, W. Cruttwell, Sherborne, 1790

Quiller-Couch, Arthur, *The Oxford Book of Victorian Verse*, Clarendon Press, Oxford, 1912

Richards, Denzil, *The Redruth Choral Society*, 2014

Routley, E., *Hymns and Human Life*, John Murray, 1952

Rowse A. L., *The Cornish in America*, Dyllansow Truran, 1967

Sandys, W., *Christmastide*, John Russell Smith, London, 1852

Scawen, *Antiquities Cornuontanic, Dissertation on the Cornish Tongue*, manuscript written c.1683

Stithians Local History Group, *Always Something Interesting, Still More Aspects of History in Stithians*, part three

Stithians Parish History Group, *The Book of Stithians*, Halsgrove, 1999

Tangye, M., *Victorian Redruth*, M.Tangye, 2001

Williams, D., *A Century of Song*, D. Williams, Newlyn, 2009

Wootton, B., *Pantomime Stew: An Anthology of Poetry, Doggerel and Nonsense*, Sue Luscombe, 1994

Wright, M., *Cornish Guernseys and Knit-Frocks*, Ethnographica, London, 1979

Old Cornwall, the Journal of the Federation of Old Cornwall Societies

1926, No 3, *St Day Carol*, Watson

1927, No 5, *An Old Cornish Carol Book*, Tom Miners

1927, No 5, *Tom Bawcock's Eve*, Robert Morton Nance

1929, No 9, *An Old Cornish Chres'muss*, W. Arthur Pascoe

1943, Vol 4, No 2, *Joseph Pryor of Lanner, A Cornish Harmonious Blacksmith*, Ashley Rowe

1949, Vol 4, No 9, *Some Cornish Places of Pilgrimage*, Rev J. H. Adams

1957, Vol 5, No 8, *Scawen on Carols in Cornish*, R. Morton Nance

1959, Vol 5, No 10, *Christmas Customs at Newlyn*, J. Kelynack

1962, Vol 5, No 3, *Cornish Folk Songs and Carols*, Inglis Gundry

1966, Vol 6, No 11, *Things Seen and Heard, Decoration in the Last Years of the 19th Century*, C. F. J.

1968, Vol 7, No 2, *Review of Beyond The Blaze*, Dr A.C. Todd

2011, Vol 14, No 5, *Bude-Stratton and District OCS Celebrates 50 years*, A. Aylmer

Folk Song Society Journals

1914, Vol 5, No 18, *Redruth Warzail*, C. J. Sharp

1916, Vol 5, No 20, *Carols*, C. J. Sharp

1929, Vol 8, No 33, *Cornish Carols*, Collected by J. E. Thomas & T. Miners

Other journals

Cornish Magazine, vol 7, no.8, 'Seasonal Traditions: Cornish Carols and Carol Singers', Cyrill Noall, Penpol Press, Falmouth, 1964

Journal of American Folklore, 'Songs of the Twelve Numbers and the Hebrew Chant of Echod mi Yodea', Leah Rachel Clara Yoffie, 1949

Journal of American Folklore, 'The Carol of the Twelve Numbers', William Wells Newell, 1891

Journal of the Royal Institution of Cornwall, No 70, Vol 11, 'Report of meeting of the Newquay Old Cornwall Society', October 1922, 1923

Tre, Pol and Pen, 'Cornish Carols', article, Dr Ralph Dunstan, 1928

Newspaper Articles

Almaden Times, 22.12.2005

Cornishman, 'Christmas in Newlyn Fifty Years Ago', 1931

The Cornish Post and Mining News, 25.1.1900

The Guardian Magazine, Dance Lessons for Writers, Zadie Smith, 29.10.2016

West Briton & Cornwall Advertiser, 19.12.1889

West Briton, 26.12.1889

West Briton, 'Bygone Days', Martin Matthews, 30.12.2004

West Briton, 'Cornish Carols CD sells out', 2008

West Briton, 'Half a Century at the Same Church', 2013

West Briton, 'Old Cornwall Society', article, 19.11.2015

Western Morning News, 'Days of wassailing and carolling', A. A. Clinnick, 22.12.1925

Western Morning News, 'Old Cornish Carols', Barnicoat, Polperro, 19.12.1925

Western Morning News, letter W.D. Wood-Rees, 1924

Western Morning News, BBC recording Mabe MVC, 21.12.1936

Western Morning News, Geoffry Baggs, 1968

Western Morning News, 'Sound, sound your instruments of joy!', David Oates, 18.12.2001

Western Morning News, Dancing to a New Rhythm, Simon Parker, 8.1.2002

Western Morning News, Hark it's the Sound of Christmas Past, Simon Parker, 12.12.2015

Western Morning News, 2.1.16

Discography

Brenda Wooton: *Piper's Folk*, Pipers Folk, 1968. *Starry Gazey Pie*, Sentinel, 1975. *Way Down to Lamorna*, Sentinel, 1984. *Voice of Cornwall*, Keltia Music, 1996

Cadgwith Singers, *Return to Cadgwith*, 2008

Climax Male Voice Choir, *Season's Best, the Christmas carols of Merritt and Nicholas*, Sentinel Records, 1971

Four Lanes Male Choir with Mabe Ladies Choir, Camborne Circuit Ladies Choir & Redruth Methodist Church Choir, *A Cornish Christmas with Merritt*, Paul Martyn Sound Productions, 2008

Grass Valley Cornish Carol Choir with the Grass Valley Male Voice Choir, *When Miners Sang*, 1946, 1959 & 2001

John Barber & The St Ives Minstrels, *Cornwall is Calling*, Sentinel, 1971

Kenneth Pelmear, *Carols of Cornwall, Live from Truro Cathedral*, VHF, 1982

Kescana & Pyba, *Nadelik: A Cornish Christmas*, Pyba, 2002

Keur heb Hanow, *Karolyow Nadelik*, Chris Doggett, 2015

Methodist Choirs, *Cornish Christmas*, Chough Records, Helford, date unknown

Mousehole Male Voice Choir, *Christmas with Mousehole*, Paul Martyn Sound Productions, 2013

Mousehole Male Voice Choir, *Cornish Christmas Carols*, Sound News Productions, 1970

Perraners, *A Seagull in a Pear Tree*, Kenver Easton, 2006

Peter Kennedy, *Camborne Hill, Songs and Customs from Cornwall*, 1956

Port Isaac Chorale and others, *A Port Isaac Christmas*, The Cube, 2015

Webography

Encarta Encyclopedia, 1993-2009, no longer active

www.maxhunter.missouristate.edu

www.an-daras.com

www.bodminwassail.uk

www.cornishculture.co.uk

www.digicoll.library.wisc.edu/WiscFolkSong

www.fourlanesmalechoir.com

www.hymnary.org

www.hymnsandcarolsofchristmas.com

www.jstor.org: Journal Bizarre Notes and Queries, The Carol of the 12 Numbers, Rev J. Hopkins, 1889

www.mouseholemalevoicechoir.com

www.mustrad.org.uk: Glimpses into the 19th Century Broadside Ballad Trade, R Brown, 2003

www.spellerweb.net

www.ststythiansmalechoir.org.uk

Miscellaneous

Welliver Collection, *Cornish Singers*, The Library of Congress, American Folklife Centre, USA, 1949

Calstock History Society Newsletter, 'Calstock Christmas Capers', H. James, circa 2000

R. Gool, *The Padstow Carollers*, private collection, 2015

F. Illustration references
Cover
Carollers at Hoopers Bridge, Lanivet, 1940, Kresenn Kernow.
Acknowledgements
Peter Meanwell, Collins, Linda, 2017
Linda Collins at home, Burley, Sally, 2016.
Introduction
Christmas Carols at Mount Folly, Bodmin, 1950, Kresenn Kernow.
Sally Burley, Hilary Coleman and Clive Boutle; Gorsedd Kernow, 2016.
A Brief History of Carols
Tregajorran Choir and band, 1860, from the Tregajorran Archives.
Diaspora emigration, advert, *West Briton*, 1839, Kresenn Kernow.
Early Carols In Cornwall Introduction
Davies Gilbert, circa 1823, Kresen Kernow.
Title page of Christmas Carols, Ancient and Modern, 1833, Kresenn Kernow.
Can Dilly (The Dilly Song)
Tracey Worrall & Frances Bennett, Degol Stul, 2017, Wheeler, David.
King and Queen, Degol Stul, 2017, Wheeler, David.
Go Your Way Green Leaves
Inglis Gundry, Hunt, Bob, Lockyer, Suzy, private collection.
Boilerhouse, Williams, Rick.
The Holly and the Ivy
Cornish Kissing Bush, Old Cornwall, 1966, Kresenn Kernow.
Kescana, Tagney, Jo.
St Day Carol
Carharrack and St Day Silver Band, Harry, Terry, 2017.
Boys collecting holly, 1939, Kresenn Kernow.
A Virgin Most Pure
Late 17th century notebook, Kresenn Kernow.
Carol Hymns and Hedge Choirs in Cornwall Introduction
Front cover of Barnicoat's carols, Coleman, Hilary, Kresenn Kernow.
Doidge's carol collections, 1889 and earlier, Coleman, Hilary, Kresenn Kernow.
Front cover of Heath's Cornish Carols, 1889, Coleman, Hilary, private collection.
Ralph Dunstan, 1919, Perranzabuloe Museum.
Warmington's two volumes of Cornish carols, 1912, Coleman, Hilary, Kresenn Kernow.

The Angels' Song (Glory, Glory)
R. L. Lowry, The Cyber Hymnal.
Singers, Kings Arms, Burley, Sally, private collection, 2016.
Awake Ye Nations (Wakey, Wakey)
Tregajorran Chapel Choir, 1947, from the Tregajorran Archives.
Moonta poster, Pryor, Oswald, Pryor, Geoff.
Calm On the Listening Ear of Night
Christmas Welcome covers, 1893 & circa 1920s, Kresenn Kernow.
Johnny Thomas, Pryor, Oswald: Pryor, Geoff.
Edmund Hamilton Sears, Dictionary of Unitarian and Universalist Biography.
Flaming Seraphs (The Stratton Carol)
Bude and Stratton Old Cornwall Society singers: Burley, Sally, 2016.
Bude and Stratton Old Cornwall Society banner, Burley, Sally, 2016.
Hail Sacred Day, Auspicious Morn
Front cover of Merritt's Carols, circa 1920s, Coleman, Hilary.
Inside Paynters Lane End Chapel, Burley, Sally, 2016.
Paynters Lane End Chapel, Coleman, Hilary, 2017.
Hark the Glad Sound (Merritt)
Ivor Richardson and Hilary Coleman, Burley, Sally, 2016.
Thomas Merritt, St Illogan Church website.
Harmony Choir and crowd, Falmouth, December 2016, Dyer, Jen.
Hark the Glad Sound (Port Isaac)
Port Isaac Chorale, Burley, Sally, 2015.
Port Isaac Chorale, circa 1990s, Townsend, Janet, private collection.
Old Port Isaac Choir, circa 1930s, Townsend, Janet, private collection.
Hark What Music
Oswald Pryor cartoon, Pryor, Geoff.
Canoryon Trewoon, Coleman, Hilary, 2015.
Troon Toc H Choir, 1974, Hocking, Jill, private collection.
Hellesveor
Hellesveor Chapel, Coleman, Hilary.
Colan Williams book cover, circa 1920s, Wheeler, David.
St Ives carollers, Thomas, Bill, 2005.
Tommy Banfield, Cornish Gorsedd.
Karol, Karol Kristyons (Carol, Carol Christians)
Carol singers at Hoopers Bridge, Lanivet, 1940: Kresenn Kernow.
Keur Heb Hanow, Bridge Chapel, Wheeler, David & Tina, 2015.
Rouse, Rouse
Padstow carollers, Neale, Kate, 2010.
Cover to *Strike Sound*, 1965, Coleman, Hilary.
Sapphire Throne
Clarence & Christabel Maynard, Maynard, Clive, private collection.
Flowerpot Chapel, Redruth, Redruth OPC website
Tereba Nessa, Burley, Sally, 2015.

Bridge Chapel, Hedge, Terry, 2017.

Seraphic Minstrels (Sound, Sound)

Halzephron Inn pub sign, Burley, Sally, 2015.

Porthleven Shoemaker's Shop Choir, 1950s, West Briton, 2004.

Paul Collins and wife, at Halzephron Inn, Burley, Sally, 2015.

Star of Bethlehem (Lo the Eastern)

Woolcock, Helston, Broadsheet, 1840-80, Broadside Ballads Online, Bodleian Library.

Commercial Inn, St Just Feast, 2012, Burley, Sally.

Nicholas' carols covers, circa 1960s, Coleman, Hilary, Kresen Kernow.

While Shepherds Watched in Cornwall Introduction

Brenda Wooton, Ellery-Hill, Sue, private collection.

Bolingey Version

Red River Singers, Bridge Chapel, Wheeler, Tina, 2016.

Boscastle Jack

Boscastle Buoys, Boscastle Harbour, Boscastle Buoys.

We'll Never Say Goodbye words, Heart Cheering Songs, 1899, private collection.

Lyngham

Guising in Calstock, 1980s, Coleman, Hilary, private collection.

Singers in The Tamar Inn, Calstock, Coleman, Hilary, 2016.

Newlyn Version

Mousehole Male Voice Choir, Paul Church, Burley, Sally, 2015.

Two Pendeen Versions and One from Treen

Pendeen Miners choir, Williams, Rick, private collection.

Stithians Version

St Stythians MVC, Stithians Ladies Choir, Burley, Sally, 2015.

Stithians UMFC Choir, 1901, *The Book of Stithians*, Halsgrove.

Logan Rock Inn, Hedge, Terry, 2017.

'Tis Christmas Time

Polperro Fisherman's Choir, Polperro chapel, Burley, Sally, 2015.

Manuscripts of Behold, Coleman, Hilary, 2016.

Jim Curtis and knit-frock, 1860s, Cornish Guernseys and Knit-Frocks, 1979, Mary Wright.

Wassails and Winter Festivals in Cornwall Introduction

Grampound Wassailers, 1930, Old Cornwall, John Stephens, 1932.

Grampound Wassail Bowl, Davies, Rachel, private collection, 2006.

Raffidy Dumitz Band, Degol Stul, Wheeler, David & Tina, 2017.

Bodmin Wassail

Harold's chair, Burley, Sally, 2016.

Mayor pouring drink for Wassailers, 1953, Kresenn Kernow.

Bodmin Wassail bowl, Burley, Sally, 2016.

Bodmin Wassailers, Burley, Sally, 2016.

Cotehele Wassail

Rosie Fierek, Burley, Sally, 2016.

The Gurt 'Oss, Cotehele, Burley, Sally, 2016.

Redruth Wassail
Redruth Wassail bowl, 2015, Cornish Culture Association website.
Tom Bawcock
Starry Gazey pie lights, Burley, Sally, 2015.
Morton Nance, Kresenn Kernow.
Wassail the Silver Apple
Dawn Chorus at Tremenheere, Burley, Sally, 2015.
Mike O'Connor; O'Connor, Mike, private collection; 2009.
Christmas Bells
Four Lanes Square; Coleman, Hilary; 2015.
Four Lanes Male Choir; Coleman, Hilary; 2015.
A Cornish Christmas with Merritt; Coleman, Hilary; 2017.
Appendices
Map of places visited; Coleman, Hilary.

Index

Track Listing

CD One

1. ***Hark the Glad Sound*** from A Cornish Christmas with Merritt, Four Lanes Male Voice Choir, Mabe Ladies Choir, Camborne Circuit Ladies Choir & Redruth Methodist Church Choir, 2008
2. ***Can Dilly (The Dilly Song)*** Members of the Red River Singers and friends at Degol Stul, Heartlands, Pool, January 2017
3. ***Go Your Way Green Leaves*** Boilerhouse and other singers at the Dock Inn, Penzance, December 2015
4. ***The Holly and the Ivy*** Kescana, Lostwithiel, November 2016
5. ***St Day Carol*** Singers with Carharrack and St Day Silver Band, St Day Square, December 2015
6. ***A Virgin Most Pure*** Singers at the Countryman Inn, Piece, December 2016
7. ***The Angels' Song (Glory, Glory)*** Singers at Picrous Eve, Kings Arms, Luxulyan, December 2016
8. ***Awake Ye Nations (Wakey, Wakey)*** Tregajorran Singers, Tregajorran Square, Christmas Eve, 2015
9. ***Calm on the Listening Ear of Night*** The Washaway West Gallery Choir, Pencarrow House, December 2015
10. ***Flaming Seraphs (The Stratton Carol)*** The Bude and Stratton Old Cornwall Society Singers, The Parkhouse Centre, Bude, 2016
11. ***Hail Sacred Day, Auspicious Morn*** Augmented choir, Paynters Lane End Chapel, Illogan, November 2016
12. ***Hark the Glad Sound (Merritt)*** The Harmony Choir, Falmouth, Christmas Eve, 2016
13. ***Hark the Glad Sound (Port Isaac)*** Port Isaac Chorale, The Old Temperance Hall, Port Isaac, 2015
14. ***Hark What Music*** Canoryon Trewoon, Camborne, Christmas Eve, 2015
15. ***Hellesveor*** St Ives Combined Choirs, Fore Street Chapel, St Ives, December 2015

16. ***Karol, Karol Kristyon (Carol, Carol Christians)*** Keur Heb Hanow, Bridge Chapel, 2015

CD Two

1. ***Rouse Rouse*** Padstow Carollers, Padstow, December 2015
2. ***Sapphire Throne*** Tereba Nessa, Bridge Chapel, December 2015
3. ***Seraphic Minstrels (Sound, Sound)*** The Cadgwith Singers, Halzephron Inn, December 2015
4. ***Star of Bethlehem (Lo The Eastern)*** Members of the Cape Cornwall Singers & friends at The Kings Arms, St Just, Feast Day November 2012
5. ***Bolingey version of While Shepherds Watched*** Red River Singers, Bridge Chapel, December 2016
6. ***Boscastle Jack*** The Boscastle Buoys, The Napoleon Inn, Boscastle, 2016
7. ***Lyngham*** Singers in The Tamar Inn, Calstock, Boxing Day, 2016
8. ***Newlyn version of While Shepherds Watched*** Mousehole MVC, Paul Church, December 2015
9. ***Pendeen version of While Shepherds Watched*** Boilerhouse and other singers, The Dock Inn, Penzance, December 2015
10. ***Stithians version of While Shepherds Watched***, St Stythians MVC & Stithians Ladies Choir, Stithians Village Hall, December 2015
11. ***'Tis Christmas Time*** The Polperro Fishermen's Choir, Polperro Chapel, December 2015
12. ***Bodmin Wassail First Song and The Old Song*** The Bodmin Wassailers, 6th January 2016
13. ***Cotehele Wassail*** Calstock Rubber Band and wassailers, Cotehele Orchards, St Dominic, December 2016
14. ***Redruth Wassail*** Raffidy Dumitz and wassailers Redruth November 2015
15. ***Tom Bawcock*** Mousehole MV C and other singers, Tom Bawcock's Eve, Mousehole Harbour, December 2015
16. ***Wassail the Silver Apple*** Dawn Chorus, Kitchen Café, Tremenheere Sculpture Park, Penzance December 2015
17. ***Christmas Bells*** Four Lanes MVC, Four Lanes Square, Christmas Morning 2015